Assisted dying

A Quaker exploration

Edited by

Quentin Fowler, Barbara & Paul Henderson,

Judy Kessler and Jill Page

Published by Leeds Area Quaker Meeting

Carlton Hill Meeting House

188 Woodhouse Lane

Leeds LS2 9DX

2016

ISBN 978-0-9934947-0-3

Cover design by Ben Francis

Printed and bound by

Quacks Books, 7 Grape Lane, York YO1 7HU

Contents

Appendices

Acknowledgements

The task of compiling this collection of articles has been helped enormously by the enthusiasm and patience of the contributors. We are extremely grateful to them for their application and co-operation over many months. It has been a joy to work with them.

We were fortunate to have the knowledge and expertise of two experienced Quakers: Stevie Krayer (Southern Marches Area Quaker Meeting) was the reader of all the contributions and we are most grateful for her wise suggestions. We thank Alice Hamar (Leeds Area Quaker Meeting) who proof-read the whole document and her skill and attention to detail has been invaluable.

We thank Ben Francis for designing the book's cover. His involvement is particularly gratifying because he was an early member of the Leeds working party on end-of-life care. We also thank other earlier members of the group: Philomena O'Hare and Gillian Oakley. Ray Middleton provided website support and we are grateful to him.

Financial assistance to cover the production and distribution costs of the publication has been provided by the Sir James Reckitt Charity, the Sessions Book Trust and Leeds Area Quaker Meeting (LAQM). We are most grateful to them.

Finally we give our thanks and appreciation to LAQM for the consistent and helpful support it has given to our work over several years. Its commitment and involvement has been a solid rock on which the work of preparing this publication has been able to depend.

Preface

The Yorkshire Quaker, Joseph Wood (1750–1821), wrote: 'When we fall asleep we know not that we must ever open our eyes until we open them in Eternity'. Many of us might expect to live to an advanced age and be blessed with a 'good death', of the sort described by Joseph Wood. However, for some of us, life itself can become a challenge, with every breath being one of pain and suffering. Members of Leeds Area Meeting end-of-life care group have engaged with this issue for many years. This booklet has arisen out of their concern for end-of-life care and particularly assisted dying.

As the co-clerks of Leeds Area Quaker Meeting, we have witnessed the sensitivity of our Friends while they developed this concern. In our Area Meeting, and beyond, this work has led to an examination of conscience. It has acted as a reminder of the efforts of Friends and others who were fundamental to the establishment of hospices such as Wheatfields in Leeds, and of those involved in palliative care. As an Area Meeting we have tried to work out the best way forward for this concern and we have sought, in the words of the Quaker, Isaac Penington (1616–1679), to uphold each other 'with a tender hand', even when — particularly when — we have been in disagreement.

These specially commissioned essays provide a space for us to consider and re-consider our confused and conflicted notions about death, dying, and end-of-life care. From different vantage points and in a spirit of deep seeking, the contributors prompt us to contemplate difficult aspects of our own lives and of those around us, and to work out where we stand, or might stand, as Quakers.

Robert Keeble and Veronica O'Mara

Contributors

Jan Arriens lives in Shropshire on the Welsh border. Of Dutch parents, he spent the first 10 years of his working life as a diplomat for Australia. In his mid-30s he set up as a freelance translator in Britain, and has been a Quaker for nearly 30 years. In 1988 he founded Lifelines, whose members correspond with prisoners on death row.

Rosemary Daley is a member of Keighley Meeting, though recently she moved to Hebden Bridge. She worked in palliative medicine for twenty-five years. While now enjoying a more domestic life, she has a familiarity with death which she feels is liberating but also sometimes uncomfortable.

Quentin Fowler spent his whole working life in the probation Service. He held a variety of managerial positions before retiring in 1995. He has been a member of the Society of Friends since 1993, during which time he has been Clerk of Leeds Area Quaker Meeting and Chairman of the Board of Governors of Breckenbrough, a Quaker special school.

Harvey Gillman was for eighteen years outreach secretary for British Quakers. He has written extensively and led workshops on the Quaker movement, spirituality, mysticism, and language. Recently he has given a series of thoughts for the day on local radio, and has helped to found the Open Door for Palestine and Israel, a joint group of Quakers from Brighton and Lewes Meetings. He is also the convenor of Quakers with Jewish Connections.

Barbara Henderson has taught all age groups from three to sixty-three. She has been involved in a variety of voluntary groups. As a trustee of Breckenbrough School, she set up a successful marketing initiative at a time when the school was in difficulties due to the government policy of inclusion in mainstream schools. She started going to Quaker Meeting with neighbours when she was six and is now a member of Ilkley Meeting.

Paul Henderson worked in community development as a practitioner, trainer and manager in the UK and the rest of Europe. He has written and edited many publications on both community development and social policy. When he retired in 2006 he became a trustee of the Joseph Rowntree Charitable Trust for six years. He is a member of Ilkley Meeting and is currently Clerk.

Judy Talbot Kessler lives in Leeds and is a member of Carlton Hill Quaker Meeting. She has worked overseas, mainly in education, community work, mediation, counselling and hospital chaplaincy. She was co-organiser of the Quaker conference on death and dying in 2012 and has conducted research on assisted dying for an MA in Social Research.

Alison Leonard has written fiction, poetry and drama for children and adults, including plays and stories for BBC radio. A Quaker since the age of 24, she is an associate tutor for Woodbrooke Quaker Study Centre in Birmingham and a founder member of the Quaker Concern around Dying and Death.

Jeff McMahan is White's Professor of Moral Philosophy at the University of Oxford. He is the author of *The Ethics of Killing: Problems at the Margins of Life* (OUP, 2002) and *Killing in War* (OUP, 2009).

Mike Nellis is Emeritus Professor of Criminal and Community Justice at the University of Strathclyde, and attends Glasgow Quaker Meeting. He was formerly a social worker with young offenders in London, studied at the Institute of Criminology in Cambridge, and was involved in the training of probation officers at the University of Birmingham. He has written widely on penal reform, the probation service and alternatives to imprisonment.

Jill Page worked as a religious studies teacher until the birth of her three sons. She retrained as a teacher of the deaf, working peripatetically with pre-school children and their families. Jill was then elected to Leeds City Council and, among other things, chaired the Women's Committee. In 2010 she was received into membership at Carlton Hill Meeting and has served as an Overseer.

Tom Shakespeare is Professor of Disability Research at Norwich Medical School, University of East Anglia. He has written widely on disability studies and bioethics. His books include *Disability Rights and Wrongs* (2006) and *The Sexual Politics of Disability (*1996*)*. He is a member of Norwich Quaker Meeting.

Martin Schweiger is a doctor. After qualifying in Leeds he worked at Airedale Hospital in West Yorkshire. This was followed by seven years in Bangladesh. On returning to Yorkshire he became a public health physician. He is a member of Roundhay Quaker Meeting, Leeds.

Anne Wade became a Quaker in 1957 and is now a member of Ealing Quaker Meeting. She was a nurse and adolescent psychotherapist and she has studied linguistics. She has fought passionately all her life for children and young people to be treated for their individual needs, especially with regard to education and child protection.

Benjamin Wood lectures in theology and religious studies at the University of Chester. Until recently, he was the lead researcher on the project 'What Next for Individualism? Issues for Political Theology and Public Life' at the Lincoln Theological Institute, University of Manchester. He is a sub-editor on the blog *Political Theology Today* and a member of the Quaker Committee for Christian and Interfaith Relations.

Introduction

Barbara and Paul Henderson

The issue of assisted dying evokes passionate responses from people who are both for and against the argument. The demonstrators from both sides who held up angry placards outside Parliament in September 2015, when the Private Member's Bill on assisted dying was brought before the House of Commons, are testament to this. Many people are intensely committed to their position. Either they believe that assisted dying is abusing the sanctity of life, allowing doctors and lawyers to 'play God' while not respecting the natural order of life and death; or they think that individuals are subjected to unnecessary suffering, with doctors using developments in medical science to sustain life and disallow the individual the right to choose his or her own destiny.

Assisted dying has thus become a major public issue. Reports, articles and correspondence about it appear with increasing frequency in the media. A wide range of organisations and individuals are involved: terminally ill patients, faith groups, doctors, lawyers, campaigning organisations and academics. The usually private domain of attitudes towards death and dying has become a subject for important debate in society.

Some Quakers are beginning to become engaged with issues surrounding death and dying, of which assisted dying is one aspect. Other faith groups have debated assisted dying, notably the Anglicans, Unitarians and Jews in Britain. The Unitarians were the first faith group to say openly they believe that people have the right to choose how to end their lives.

The dilemma of assisted dying has deep moral implications and is complex both for individual and collective discernment. We hope that this publication will help Friends in their consideration of the issue.

The purpose of the book is twofold:

- To be a resource for Quakers who wish to consider the issue of assisted dying, either for themselves or their loved ones if and when the choice of assisted dying becomes available, or because they think that the Society of Friends should consider taking a public position on the issue.

- To help stimulate reflection and discussion in local and area meetings, particularly in relation to the dilemmas referred to above.

In this introduction we give a short background to assisted dying, briefly summarising the legal situation in the UK. We explain the origins of the booklet and place it in a wider Quaker context. Finally, we introduce the topics covered by the contributors. We will be using the blanket term 'assisted dying' as used by Lord Falconer in the Bill he introduced (see below).

What are the reasons for the increased media interest in assisted dying? Three factors seem to have been of central importance:

- People are living longer and the proportion of elderly people in the population will continue to grow. The number of very old people is growing particularly fast – the number of those over eighty-five in the UK is predicted to double in the next twenty years and treble in the next thirty. People are more likely to die of serious illnesses, which could mean living with the knowledge of impending death and increasing debility for years.

- Medical advances mean that people can be kept alive much longer than previously. In his series of Reith lectures in 2014 Atul Gawande, a New York doctor and writer, used the term medicalised mortality. One response to this development has been the growth of palliative care:
http://bbc.co.uk/programmes/b00729d9

- Health and social care services have sought to respond to the above trends. However, the period of austerity since 2008 has seen severe public expenditure cuts, especially in social care. This has resulted in growing pressures and demands on community services. The extremely high cost of care provision for the growing number of elderly people leads those who are against assisted dying to fear, understandably, that these people will be seen as a burden on society.

The above, in summary form, provides some initial background to the issue of assisted dying. Careful debate is essential, alongside the capacity to listen to a multiplicity of viewpoints. Before discussing the Quaker context it is important to present the legal situation on assisted dying.

The Suicide Act 1961 – which applies only in England and Wales – decriminalised the act of suicide so that anyone who failed in the attempt to kill him or herself would no longer be prosecuted. As subsequently amended, it also states that a person commits an offence if he or she 'does an act capable of encouraging or assisting the suicide or attempted suicide of another person'. It continues by

3

stating that 'a person convicted of such an offence is liable to imprisonment for a term not exceeding 14 years'. Under the law in Scotland a person who assists a suicide might be charged with murder, culpable homicide or no offence depending upon the facts of each case.

In the course of the present century, attempts have been made to change the law relating to assisted dying. In February 2003 Lord Joffe proposed, as a Private Member's Bill, the Assisted Dying for the Terminally Ill Bill, which would legalise physician-assisted dying. Then, in the House of Lords in June 2014, Lord Falconer tabled an Assisted Dying Bill which mirrored the law as enacted in Oregon – for details please refer to Appendix (i). However, neither Bill became law, in part through lack of parliamentary time. In September 2015, Rob Marris MP introduced a Private Member's Bill in the House of Commons on assisted dying. It was defeated by a substantial majority, on a free vote.

Attempts have been made to clarify how the law on assisting someone to commit suicide might be enforced. In February 2010, the Director of Public Prosecutions issued the prosecuting policy on cases of 'Encouraging or Assisting Suicide'. The policy includes a detailed list of public interest factors that will influence the decision on whether or not to prosecute someone for assisting a suicide. A prosecution is less likely if the assisted person made a voluntary, well-informed decision to end his or her life, and if the assister was wholly motivated by compassion.

The process of a Quaker concern[1]

As part of the Leeds Area Quaker Meeting (LAQM) consideration of end-of-life care, a working party was set up in the autumn of 2010 to investigate a Quaker concern held by Quentin Fowler, a member of Adel Local Meeting. The concern arose after he watched a television programme called 'A short stay in Switzerland'. It was a docudrama which told of how a doctor in Bristol who had a terminal illness travelled to the Dignitas clinic in Zurich to end her life (assisted dying is not illegal in Switzerland). Quentin was very moved by what he saw. He considered that there must be a better way to end one's life in these circumstances. He brought his concern to Adel Meeting who accepted it; a minute was agreed and sent to LAQM. It was at that point that LAQM set up a working party on end-of-life care.

At the meetings held by the group Friends talked of their own experience of the death of family and friends, their fears and hopes for their own deaths and what they could do to try and enable what they saw as a good death. This was a time and process where trust and confidence was built up between group members. Some Friends were able to speak publicly for the first time about their anguish and grief.

In December 2011 a one-day workshop was held; this involved more than thirty people. The following questions were addressed:

[1] The Quaker meaning of a concern is different from the normal use of the word. A Quaker concern is a deeply felt and spiritually inspired sense of personal responsibility to do something about a problem, situation or a need. It is usually held by an individual and may, on occasion, lead to action by a Local or Area Meeting or Yearly Meeting.

- What would be a good death for you?
- How can you put things in place to enable this?
- What barriers would prevent you from achieving this?
- What practical steps can you take to ensure a good death?

These questions arose from the experiences of the group about what had been helpful in dealing with the emotions and pain of the deaths of others.

In discussion at the end of the workshop there was a request that a day conference be organised, with experts to talk on the topic of death and dying. The conference was held in May 2012 and was attended by more than 100 people, Quakers and non-Quakers. Professor Emily Jackson (London School of Economics) spoke on the law as it pertained to assisted dying in the UK and Professor Jan Bernheim (Belgium) spoke about the Benelux system of physician-assisted dying – see Appendix (i). Other speakers talked about palliative care and the spiritual parameters of death and dying. Debbie Purdy spoke in a small group about her campaign to allow her partner to accompany her to Switzerland without fear of prosecution. The participants separated into small groups and considered topics relating to other issues: thinking about the Hippocratic Oath, challenging the law, soul midwifery[2], complications of dementia and the 'slippery slope' argument – the fear that vulnerable people will be persuaded to end their lives. For DVD see: http://www.leedsquakers.org/activities/deathanddying

When the working party reported back to LAQM, it planned to lay down the concern. However it was asked to look further into the

[2] Soul midwives are holistic and spiritual companions to anyone at the end of their life.

question of end-of-life care. Drawing on research being undertaken by one of its members, focus groups were held at six of the local meetings in Leeds in 2013 and a questionnaire on end-of-life issues was circulated. Ninety-eight Friends responded. The findings of the survey were very helpful to the working party because they pointed to the level of concern felt by Friends on the issue of assisted dying. The majority of respondents wanted assisted dying to become law, with only a small number being against it or undecided. The researcher noted that the findings did not necessarily indicate an overwhelming agreement amongst Leeds Quakers in favour of assisted dying for themselves but more that it was felt that the choice should be available. A summary of the research findings can be found in Appendix (ii).

On various occasions members of the working party gave presentations about the work undertaken:

- A special interest meeting at Britain Yearly Meeting (BYM) in 2013
- A meeting of Quakers in Yorkshire in 2013
- A special interest meeting at BYM gathering at Bath in 2014
- A meeting of Quaker Life Central Committee in 2014

The working party reported to LAQM in May 2014 and it was at this point that a decision was made to send a minute to Meeting for Sufferings about the concern. A special area meeting, attended by twenty-eight Friends, was held at which, after a period of deep spiritual discernment, a minute was prepared. The last two paragraphs of the minute read:

> Throughout our deliberations what has been apparent is our sense of great compassion for those suffering at the

end of their lives and the need for palliative care. We reflected on why the state of end-of-life care in Britain today leads some to consider the issue of assisted dying as the preferred option.

Leeds Area Quaker Meeting feels that it has tested the end-of-life concern, including the matter of assisted dying. LAQM agrees that this minute should be sent to Meeting for Sufferings requesting that Sufferings consider adopting this concern with the possibility of establishing the Quaker view on assisted dying within the context of end-of-life care.

At its December 2014 meeting, Meeting for Sufferings acknowledged the importance of end-of-life concerns, including assisted dying, and encouraged Friends to talk more about the issues. It was after this that the working party decided, with the support of LAQM, to produce this book.

Challenges and dilemmas for Quakers

Quaker testimonies do not exist in any rigid, written form, nor are they imposed in any way. The word testimony describes the way that Friends testify or bear witness to their beliefs in their everyday life. The profound teachings and lives of Friends over the last 350 years, found in the book *Quaker faith & practice* (2013)[3], provide us with a deep inner conviction and challenge us to try to discern how we live our lives. Arising from an understanding of certain

[3]*Quaker faith & practice* is the book of Britain Yearly Meeting. It includes *Advices & Queries* and Quaker testimonies and reflections.

values and principles that are central to Quaker faith, they encourage us to put faith into practice, living our witness, often with great difficulty.

> Quakers' understanding of faith is that true human fulfilment comes from an attempt to live life in the spirit of love and truth and peace, answering that of God in everyone. These beliefs spring from a sense of equality, compassion and seeing the sacred in all life. The testimonies are about Quakers' commitment to those beliefs. Naturally, our day-to-day practice of them faces us with many dilemmas and compromises.
> www.bathquakermeeting.org.uk

Sometimes the issues facing society are deeply challenging. Reaching an individual decision on an issue such as same-sex marriage or assisted dying can be soul-searchingly difficult (see contribution by Harvey Gillman) and, as Harvey says:

> each of us … will, in hope, faith, love and trust, do what we feel we have to do and take the consequences … Even a change in the law will not take away the pain of decision-making.

From the Leeds research on assisted dying, we can see how some Friends express their feelings and thoughts on the issue and we now share some examples of what was written and spoken. The quotations underline the extent to which the testimonies, and how we interpret them, evolve and change. They also emphasise the challenges faced by individual Friends in responding to these issues.

> I wonder whether I would trust to put myself in God's will. I think that's part of it. I am not sure that it has anything to do with the corporate, but it does have to do with the individual. The right to make their own choice, in their own way, as to what happens next.

> We have got to work out a collective perspective on this very complex issue… I don't think we want to end up as atomised individuals where a, b and c do their own thing.

The Peace Testimony, arising from the declaration written in 1660, has evolved into being an active expression of how we live in the world, challenging us in every generation. We believe that everyone can respond to the spirit of God within us (whoever and whatever we believe that to be). However, the Peace Testimony is not simple and Friends will not all have the same understanding of how they should respond to it and bear witness to it, particularly with an issue such as assisted dying.

Our deep conviction of 'that of God in everyone' and the sacredness of life immediately leads us away from the idea of assisting a death. It has encouraged Quakers to engage in practical work in areas affected by wars while at the same time searching for alternatives to all kinds of violence and conflict, both individual and international. Most Quakers are pacifists.

> I am utterly opposed to all attempts to make it legally acceptable to take another's life or to help another take their own life. Such acts of murder are against the Peace Testimony.

However, Quakers suffered great hardship for their beliefs in the seventeenth century. They have, since then, concentrated much of their witness on the relief of suffering at all levels. Involvement in prison reform and the abolitionist movement are testaments to this. This love and compassion might lead us to believe in relieving suffering through assisted dying. Some Friends spoke and wrote with passion about watching loved ones suffer. One Friend wrote:

> I know she was in terrible pain… And that made her death and everything about it really hard.

> My wife was crying out for the last three days and looking back I wish I had done what I shouldn't do in law.

All Quaker testimonies (Truth, Equality and Simplicity being the other main ones) guide us spiritually towards seeking a way forward. As with Friends in the past, we are continually being challenged to interpret our testimonies in relation to complex issues of society at large. Responses from Leeds Friends highlight the dilemmas:

> Simplicity: It may…be against the testimony to simplicity in certain circumstances to prolong life by artificial means.

> Equality: Legalising assisted dying would make it more likely that disadvantaged and vulnerable people would experience discrimination and untimely death.

> Truth: We have this image of how we think it is going to be and more often than not it isn't.

In a Meeting for Worship for Business, where there may be strongly divided opinions and difficult decisions to be made, we are called upon as Quakers to listen with loving acceptance to the leadings of others. We do not use a voting system but continue to share beliefs and opinions until the clerk feels that a corporate sense of the meeting has been reached and gradually a minute is written. A Friend said:

> I try to live up to Quaker testimonies. I try to make rational decisions and I want the same at my death.

This publication

We wanted most of the contributors to be members of the Society of Friends and all except one are. We were also anxious to obtain a breadth of opinions and to have a collection of articles addressing the issue of assisted dying from a variety of perspectives: personal, medical, legal, philosophical, theological. Having such a mix of articles would, we thought, provide insights, knowledge and stimulus for readers. Before inviting writers to contribute, we did not ask for a particular opinion to be expressed, with the exception of one writer because we wanted at least one contribution strongly questioning assisted dying.

We begin with a discussion by *Harvey Gillman* on the use of testimonies for individual and corporate discernment when reaching a difficult decision. He describes the Quaker deliberation that took place on the issue of same-sex marriage. *Alison Leonard* then reflects on her personal responses to the idea of assisted dying and explains the work undertaken by the national group, Quaker Concern around Dying and Death. There follow two articles written from a medical perspective: *Rosemary Daley* is a former consultant in palliative medicine. She shares her doubts about assisted dying while, at the same time, noting the complicated nature of the issue; *Martin Schweiger* writes as a consultant in public health and argues for more choice for patients; these contributions are followed by an exploration of assisted dying by sociologist *Tom Shakespeare* within the context of disability. *Mike Nellis* then considers the issue of assisted dying from a criminological perspective, looking particularly at the Belgian experience. We have two contributions examining assisted dying and ethics: *Benjamin Wood* explores Quaker beliefs and thinking, the traditions and language of our spirituality and the challenge and consolation of Quaker ethics; *Jeff McMahan* summarises the case for assisted dying from a moral philosopher's perspective, ending by addressing the problem of dementia and assisted dying. This focus on dementia is continued in the next contribution, written by *Quentin Fowler*. He gives his personal viewpoint on dementia and assisted dying, looking at various options and prioritising the principles of autonomy and compassion. At the end of this article, *Judy Kessler* describes a situation in her local meeting, shares her thoughts and explains her position. After that we include the article 'Life and Death' by *Anne Wade*, as published in *the Friend*. Finally *Jan Arriens* makes connections between prisoners on death row in the USA and assisted dying. He emphasises the need to respect different perspectives on assisted dying, and for our discernment to draw heavily on our testimonies, all in a state of spiritual grace.

In Appendix (i) we summarise the legal situation with regard to assisted dying in England and Wales and also Scotland. We then describe attempts to change and clarify the law in the UK, the law and practice in Oregon and legislation in other USA states, and in Switzerland, Belgium, Holland and Luxembourg. Details of four relevant UK organisations are also provided. There is a summary of the Leeds research in Appendix (ii), followed by a selected bibliography.

Testimony and discernment

Harvey Gillman

I felt a certain reluctance when I was invited to write this article. Once, when asked by a member of my meeting who belongs to an organisation supporting voluntary euthanasia what my feelings were concerning this subject, I had to admit I did not really know, as I could see arguments on every side. Reflecting later, it came to me that it is one thing to have a theology of life, a system of ethics, even a 'feeling' on this subject in the abstract; it would be quite another if I were sitting at the bedside of someone in great pain who was begging that she be assisted to die. Moreover, I do not know how I would actually react to an overwhelming painful disease that was destroying my own body and sense of self.

What I am offering here then is a series of general reflections and questions on how Quakers, corporately and individually, might make decisions in the light of Quaker testimonies. However, I do not pretend to know how in particular circumstances I myself would act. I would pray to have the grace and the strength to act well and with authenticity, in accordance with my basic convictions about the sanctity of human life and the honouring of each person as made in the image of God. But until I am really there, I do not know how I would react.

I begin with some questions, posed to all people who are part of religious movements, and to myself as a member of Friends.

Does the fact that I am a member of a religious organisation, albeit a creedless and non-dogmatic one, influence the way I live my life, how I make decisions for myself, and how I participate in the life of the group? If not, what is the point of belonging? If it does, on what basis do I make the decision, what importance do I give to the discernment of the group, and how does it come about that several people starting from the same point – a biblical text, a shared assumption about the world, a communal discernment about the value of peace and justice, and so forth – actually end up by reaching different conclusions?

Of course much depends on how much importance I lay on a particular decision. There is a difference as to whether the group is choosing a new carpet for the meeting house, making a representation to government on issues of justice and poverty, or affirming its gay, lesbian and transgender members. The principle of group discernment may be similar in each case, but my involvement on a spiritual or emotional level may well differ according to the issue.

In making such decisions, we need to have a good deal of self-awareness. And ask ourselves some basic questions. Do we use the external trappings of religion to bolster and justify our own particular egos or wills? Do we interpret theology through the lens of our particular psychologies, social circumstances, needs and cravings? Do we talk of the will of God and act as though this were synonymous with our own desires and conditionings? Is God just another word for conscience? Or is there indeed some transcendent force to which we can turn and which can give us a basis for acting and the strength to act in the world?

I remember a Friend once saying that he was a Quaker because of how he saw the world; he did not view the world in a particular way because he was a Quaker. The human precedes the religious; the religious enhances, one hopes, the depth of the human condition; gives it a language, a model, a means of reflection, a community in which to explore relationship with the divine and the self. It offers support in discerning and implementing moral choices in one's life – and also challenges them. The human asks the question; the spiritual path offers tools for exploration of possible responses. Those with whom one shares the path are interlocutors. They ask questions of one, offer enlightenment; at least one hopes they do! As a human being and as a Quaker I am suspicious of answers, especially those which precede or even ignore the questions. Even an appeal to the law is not definitive, though it may make choosing a certain action easier. For committed members of a religious organisation it is the community, its traditions and its convictions that can help us recognise the necessary questions in the first place. I suspect our lives themselves are the responses to these questions.

How do we act?

So what does my being a Quaker mean to me? I am comfortable with paradoxes, so my theology is a theology of 'the beyond within', the Inward Light, the God within and between, the sacred voice in the soul, that divine energy that despite the name we give it, is beyond names, but is the activator of human creativity. When George Fox (1624-1691) spoke of 'that of God' within, he was not offering a creed, but a call to action. We are, he told us, to 'answer' that of God. This apprehension of the here and now of the divine was a basis for a way of living. It was deepened as the worshipper waited expectantly, transcended ego, and listened. The grace received, the Light that illuminated, revealed the inner darkness but gave energy to move forward. The life lived in this faithfulness was a witness, a testimony, to this encounter.

Quaker testimonies are sometimes thought of as being good social values, like peace, justice, environmental concern, truthfulness, and simplicity. Being values they can be discussed philosophically as abstractions. They can function as creeds. We can say: I believe in peace, in justice etc. Early Quakers, however, were not concerned with creeds or abstract ethics. Rather they witnessed to the intimacy of the human-divine encounter through everyday action, irrespective of the law, in the way they spoke, dressed, conducted their meetings for worship, used their money, refused to take up arms (though the latter was not always true in the first generation as some Friends were members of Commonwealth armies!). And they suffered for their choices.

They became anti-war. They had seen how the sword was used to promote the reign of the Prince of Peace and they recognised the contradictions involved. They were anti-tithe partly because they saw with their own eyes how the poor were made poorer by the enriching of what they saw as a hireling clergy. It was only gradually that they began to reflect on the general themes of peaceful international relations (William Penn (1644–1718) and economic justice (John Bellers (1654–1725) and John Woolman (1720–1772), though the seeds are found in Fox himself. So the question is: having had my eyes opened to the world through turning to the Light within and by being faithful to the voice in my soul, how do I, indeed how do we, act in the here and now?

Decision-making, however, was never very easy. You could wait for hours on the Spirit. You could put aside ego. You did not always agree. There were dissensions and splits in the early days of the Quaker movement. The testimony against war took time to establish itself and has never become an absolute creed for all Friends. Even the role of women in the Quaker movement has evolved and been expressed in differing ways. Whenever anyone says: 'Quakers have always ...' I feel I need to reach for a history book, which usually contradicts whatever is being stated.

Testimony is also read ambiguously by the world that witnesses it. Early Friends 'went naked for a sign' against war, against slavery, against the priesthood. The society around them, however, saw loose behaviour and extreme fanaticism. That mode of behaviour soon died out. However, the dilemma between action for the sake of conscience and public perception has not. In the American Civil War, many felt it strange that Quakers did not take up arms against the institutions of slavery (actually some Quakers did fight). A peace testimony can seem to be a way of preserving injustice. This ambiguity is reflected also among Friends ourselves. I remember reading an article by an American friend who said that her opposition to the death penalty also led to her opposition to abortion, both consequences of her conviction that war and killing are against the will of God. The juxtaposition of anti-death penalty and anti-abortion might not be very common among British Friends today, but shows the ambiguity of personal conscience based on a leading of the Spirit.

One common phrase heard among Friends is that we try to discern the will of God – both in our communal business sessions, our meetings for worship for business, and in our personal lives. To put it simply we are trying to find out what God wants of us, or as some other Friends might put it, how we are being led by Spirit. But at a time when there are not many shared understandings of what or whether God is, that only opens the door to more dilemmas. Some Christians may claim that they understand the will of God by reading sacred text, but given the ambiguity of the latter, and the many differing interpretations of scripture, that again leads to further complications. Those who claim to listen to the promptings of the Inward Light open themselves to further difficulties. Is the Inward Light that of a personal God who has a will which can be known? Is it a movement into harmony with an impersonal ground of being, and how can one know when that harmony has been achieved? If God is, as is claimed by some Friends, the highest part of the human, then is the discernment of its 'will' a way of answering the question: what is the best way of acting as noble human beings in this circumstance? And in what way would the latter process differ from a totally humanist process of discernment?

Personal experience

I should like at this point to reflect how this dilemma is working its way out in my own life. In 1994 Friends were discussing the new edition of *Quaker faith & practice (Qf&p)*. Questions arose concerning Chapter 22, Close relationships. During the discussion at Britain Yearly Meeting, some homophobic comments were made and there was a small group of Friends who were opposed to a recognition of gay/lesbian relationships. I remember thinking at the time, if these relationships were not affirmed I would leave Quakers. Afterwards I reflected on the whole process with some surprise at my own reactions. Here was a gathering of Friends meeting to 'discern the will of God'. It is part of my own conviction that if such a group meets together and is really open to guidance, then one should trust the process. I believe also that even if one is not present on the day, one should trust one's fellow Friends. The whole process is based on trust. And yet deep within I was convinced that the affirmation of gay/lesbian relationships was more important than the community I had been part of for almost twenty years at that time.

At the same time I strongly believed that this affirmation of love was part of my understanding of the very heart of the Quaker movement. If this affirmation of gay/lesbian relationships were rejected, it would make me question how I had previously understood the Society. Here was a group of people believing that there was that of God in all people, that love was greater than legalism, that revelation was continuous and not bound by the dictates of two thousand years ago – and yet was finding controversial something that was now so clear to me. It was something that I had been struggling for throughout my whole life. To me it was not a simple intellectual decision; it was a life experience that was being judged, a vital principle; in the words of Julian of Norwich (the fourteenth century mystic), a revelation of divine love. A basic principle of the spiritual life is recognition of the worth of self and an honouring of the way one loves, if that way of love is creative and life-enhancing. How could that possibly be against the will of a God, whose greatest attribute is love?

On the other hand, I also had to recognise that for some people that decision was difficult. They needed to have their own revelation. They had to re-examine their relationship with sacred text and with whatever the divine meant for them. The discernment for me was how to respect those who profoundly differ from me on such a basic principle. This was hard and made me angry. Yet, the process worked and I had learned yet again that I needed to trust. The process is as important as the decision. And when, at the York Yearly

Quaker Meeting 2012, Friends decided in favour of same-sex marriage, irrespective of its legal status, I was overwhelmed. However, my partner and I, though delighted by this decision, decided not to take it up for ourselves as we were already in a civil partnership, and did not feel that a marriage ceremony would add anything to the blessings we have already received in many ways from local Quakers. We were even more pleased that Friends decided to make representation to government to change the existing law, so the spiritual discernment had political consequences. Thus my partner and I accepted the corporate leading, were very happy that this leading was shared with the world, but did not regard it as relevant for us.

As a gay man, I have had to make certain choices all my life, irrespective of how society at large views these matters, based on my own conscience and personal convictions. As a Quaker I was now having to recognise a group discernment. In the end I was overjoyed in my choice of spiritual community.

Conscience

In all of this, I keep returning to the fundamental question: how do we fragile human beings live together on this fragile earth, facing as we all do that we will die, that we often make mistakes, that as individuals and communities we are often wrong. Quakers in particular make an outrageous claim that human beings need no intermediary, that the divine, however understood, is within our very being (as well as out there in the world); that we can sit and be still and discern the divine will. How, at the same time, can we avoid arrogance, how can we keep from playing God in the world? How can we claim certain knowledge? Not only of general principles but also of how to act in particular circumstances?

It is said of the Roman Catholic Church that, in spite of canon law and the rulings of the hierarchy, conscience has a fundamental role. Is conscience, then, the same as illumination by Spirit? However, for all that is written on conscience in that tradition the community does not on the whole permit deviations from principles generally accepted by the church.

Quakers, on the other hand, put great weight on conscience, but 'a conscience illuminated by the Light' (*Qf&p* 20:45). There is, perhaps, an implicit recognition here that conscience itself is not an absolute source of knowledge. There are some consciences that are not highly developed. To rely on a conditioned conscience is fine, but all conscience may be conditioned by life experience, education, culture and so forth. It is for this reason that the Quaker tradition talks of the illuminated conscience – the conscience being the lantern, the Inward Light being the flame that burns within it. But this Light is kept burning with the help of the community, with insights from tradition, and to a turning within to a greater source – unless of course one is a humanist Quaker in which case conscience may well be all there is.

Looking back on my own life, I have to state that I remain uncertain. I accept that my conscience itself needs challenging. I can sit in worship for hours and still come away not knowing. I can listen to experts (and I do often need information to make better choices) and still remain unsure. I can be part of meetings for clearness, spend hours threshing the issue, I can listen to wise counsel – but at the end of the day, I still may not know fully what the best way forward is. The second lesson, after trust, is the need for humility. I am an intuitive. I do not always reason rationally. I have a sense of things. In fact, this sense of things is the basis of my spiritual path. This sense, this intuition, has subsequently been educated, refined, by my being in community with Friends, by my opening myself in worship, by learning to wait in spite of my great impatience. However, at the end of the day I know that this intuition itself may be faulty. Perhaps human beings will never really know the will of God but go forward in a kind of sacred agnosticism, obeying that small measure of Light within their souls. This is even more of a challenge when the decision one is making involves another person, not just oneself. In the case of assisted dying, the decisions to be taken are not the same for each person. The suffering I may experience seeing another human being, especially a beloved one, in pain, is not the same as that of the person wishing to die. Indeed I may make a decision for the other which I may not make for myself. Is that hypocrisy, a contradiction, or the ambiguity of love? In his Letter to the Galatians, Paul writes:

> But the fruit of the Spirit is love, joy, peace, forbearance, kindness, goodness, faithfulness, gentleness and self-control. Against such things there is no law.

Wonderful ways of being human. General guidelines. Against such things there is no law. But put them into practice in particular ways and law may be contravened. We are called to love, but what is the appropriate act of love in a particular circumstance? And what are the consequences of that act? It may be that meditating on this passage, like the Advices and Queries which mean so much to Quakers, is a way that may help us decide. The question is put to each of us: ok, you believe in love, in truth, in peace and so forth –

but what does that mean today in this place where you are called upon to act?

As I reflect on these issues, I am aware that I am opposed to warfare, to the death penalty, and yet not opposed to abortion, neither am I a vegetarian, though I have been one. So I guess 'life' is not an unconditional value for me. Although I take it for granted that life is sacred and in so far as it is possible is to be preserved, I still have to work out what 'sacredness' means to me in the here and now of decision-making – and to discover what the phrase 'as far as it is possible' means in a given situation (I write this knowing that some other Friends will find this a contradiction).

My conclusion, if such it is, is that as Friends we do have general principles, leadings, inspirations which we share. When we meet together to make a corporate decision we are trying to discover together how this general principle works in this particular case. We may do this through prayer, waiting on the Spirit, listening to our (illuminated) consciences, but we may not always agree. If the Society were to make a decision on the principle of assisted dying (and I do not think we could at this time), here again we would need to discern how a general stance would work itself out in particular cases. That working out is always the challenge. I suspect that is why we do not have credal testimonies but prefer advices and queries. We prefer the question: 'what does love, what does compassion require of thee ?' rather than to be told that this we must or must not do.

What does love require of thee?

This leads me to another question which I have not so far addressed: that of the paradox of human autonomy. I personally as a Quaker feel that I cannot make a decision for another person as the situation of the other is not the same as mine. Autonomy, however, assumes also that the person making a decision can do so rationally, guided by his or her faculties of reason. This itself is open to question since few of us act in a fully rational way, even if we could define rationality. At the same time I do not consider that we are fully autonomous. To be human is to be in relationship. I do not end with my skin. I believe we are part of each other and of the whole flow of life. That paradox needs to be respected.

Many years ago, when I was a student teaching English to foreigners as a vacation job, I had a conversation with a woman about suicide. She was sure that if someone wanted to kill herself, no other human should intervene. To intervene was not respectful of autonomy. I was shocked by this argument. I replied that perhaps the person wanted to commit suicide because no one in her life had ever tried to intervene. I could not imagine standing aside out of a general principle. I was also sure, however, that intervention was not the same as prevention. I had no right to forbid the decision of another human being.

So I imagine myself at the bedside of a loved one in great pain, pleading with me – 'Find a way to relieve this agony'. Palliatives are offered. We sit in worship together. I remember the words of the twentieth century French philosopher Emmanuel Levinas, that we find God in the face of the other. Here the face of God is distorted by disease. The prayer of the loved one is to end the suffering as speedily as possible. How do I best honour that divinity, respond to that prayer? Have we explored together all the options?

We are both individuals and members of each other. We are led perhaps not into sure knowledge but into the uncertainty of love. We shall need grace, forgiveness, and the loving support of our friends in whatever we decide.

At the end of the day, however, each of us in our informed, illuminated, painful solitude, even with the guidance of helpful Friends and friends around us, will, in hope, faith, love and trust, do what we feel we have to do and take the consequences. Every action is a decision, even the refusal to act. The law may offer us a framework for action, may well influence what we actually do, irrespective of what we feel called to do through love and compassion. But even a change in the law will not take away from us the pain of decision-making.

So we sit and wait. We open ourselves to the Light. We listen to each other in the silence. We reflect upon ourselves and our lives. We make sure that we are as informed as we can possibly be. We face the query: What does love require of thee? In one way or another that process lies behind the Quaker way of coming to decisions. For life and for death.

How do I feel about assisted dying?

Alison Leonard

How do I feel about assisted dying? If you asked me for my *opinion* on the issue, I would say that I am in favour of a change in the law to allow terminally ill people who cannot physically end their own lives to bring it about with the help of others, provided that the necessary safeguards are in place; and I honour and sympathise with those whose circumstances have led them to campaign for such a change in the law.

But what if I took the question literally? How do I *feel* about the question of assisted dying? Then the answer would be more complicated. For, whenever the issue comes up, I find that I have so many and such contrary feelings that I hesitate to offer an opinion at all.

Let me try to unravel these feelings.

First, I find that when I am listening to those arguing the case for assisted dying, I feel irritated – distracted from the most vital task that faces each of us: that of preparing, spiritually, emotionally and practically, for our own decline and death, and having the necessary discussions about it with family and close friends. Very few of us will need to ask someone else to help us end our lives; but every single one of us will die. Might the argument around the issue of assisted dying be a displacement activity, allowing us to engage with death but still keeping it at a distance from ourselves?

Then there is the problem with the nature of argument itself. Many studies have shown how the act of arguing about an issue tends to harden views on both sides rather than bringing people towards unity.[1] Maybe this is what makes me withdraw from the argument altogether: I want to stay flexible – uncertain, even. So when people try to persuade me of the case for assisted dying, my own attachment to the case weakens, instead of strengthening, and I even hear myself arguing the opposite case. On the other hand, when I have had the chance to listen in depth to those who oppose a change in the law, I have become more sympathetic to their feelings, without my opinion on the issue being changed.

So I find myself in a contradictory state of mind. I am a member of the organisation which campaigns for a change in the law (Dignity In Dying); my heart goes out to courageous people like Debbie Purdy and Tony Nicklinson (the right-to-die campaigners) who need such a change in the law and are denied it; I feel a great dread at the thought of being trapped in a body that merely exists, rather than lives; yet I draw back from campaigning myself, and choose to focus on the basic work of facing my own death and helping other Quakers to do the same.

I was not always so reticent on the possibility of bringing forward a death. More than twenty-five years ago I wrote a short story called *A Gold for Granny Baxter*, which was published in a local anthology. The narrator is 15 year-old Monica, whose granny has had a stroke, is in a nursing home and cannot speak or move. Granny Baxter is dismissed by the rest of the family as 'weird', but Monica

---

[1] For instance, http://www.vox.com/2014/4/6/5556462/brain-dead-how-politics-makes-us-stupid

loves her, and begins to dream about her. These dreams are about sport: her granny is winning the snooker against Dennis the Irishman, winning the boxing against Sugar Ray Leonard, even joining the Olympic teams for different kinds of sport. But at the same time Monica is visiting Granny Baxter in the nursing home and seeing her lie there, helpless and miserable. One day she hears the nurses complaining that her granny won't eat the meals they are trying to feed her. A few nights later Monica dreams of Granny Baxter doing the pole vault in the Olympics, and the dream ends in her winning a medal: the Gold. Next morning there is a phone call from the home – terribly sorry, Mrs Baxter has fallen out of bed, can't think how it happened, can the family please come immediately… Granny Baxter's own indomitable will has enabled her to achieve her death, even though she 'ought not' to have been able to do it. She has got her Gold.

In the late 1980s I was appointed to the *Quaker faith and practice* Book of Discipline Revision Committee, and became closely involved in the re-drafting of *Advices & Queries* for the 1995 edition, especially what became *A&Q* (29), (30):

> 29. Approach old age with courage and hope. As far as possible, make arrangements for your care in good time, so that an undue burden does not fall on others…

> 30. Are you able to contemplate your death and the death of those closest to you? Accepting the fact of death, we are freed to live more fully. In bereavement, give yourself time to grieve. When others mourn, let your love embrace them.

I felt my own courage and hope being severely challenged. Stories circulated about the increasingly powerful role of medicine and the pharmaceutical industry in keeping people alive for longer and longer, even in the face of a patient's stated wish to slip away. As I have said above, I knew how strong was my terror of being kept expensively alive without my consent. How, if I lost my health and my autonomy, could I end my life without causing too much pain to those I love? I joined Dignity in Dying, briefly received mailings from EXIT (an end-of-life campaigning organisation), and signed a Living Will (later Advance Directive, then Decision). I wrote passionate letters to my family asking them, if I was in these circumstances, to let me go; I did not send the letters, just filed them away. But they were in no doubt about how I felt.

In 2008, I read an article in *the Friend* describing how a Friend had died in precisely the way that she had not wanted, and responded with a letter asking if it might be time to set up a group to look at current themes around dying and death. My personal fears no doubt motivated me to do this, and I probably also hoped that Friends might resolve, once and for all, the question of a change in the law to allow assisted dying. My reasoning mind, though, saw that we should give priority to preparation for our own deaths and the deaths of those closest to us.

Listening to others

The pile of responses to my letter to *the Friend* grew larger, and led to the foundation of the Quaker Concern around Dying and Death (QDD) group. At its early gatherings, I began to trust others enough to take a closer look at some of my attitudes. Gradually I discerned the reason why my fears were so strong: it was the simple, biographical fact that I had spent nine years of my childhood

32

unhappily in a boarding school for girls, and I was desperately afraid of spending years in a similar institution at the far end of my life. I would, simply, rather die.

Relaxing among QDD Friends who rapidly became friends, I was able to listen more carefully to the feelings and attitudes of others – most of them completely different from my own, and as deeply based in their experiences as my own were in mine.

This is a classic Quaker discovery, and it led to more and wider discoveries.

In my local area there was an active debating society, and they invited me to contribute to a discussion on the issue of assisted dying. On this occasion the debating society had decided to lay aside their usual confrontational arrangements, and instead give each contributor a measured length of time to make their point without being interrupted. This rather Quakerly format allowed me to hear the points made by those who disagreed with me, and understand more profoundly why some people are so against a change in the law. Some – especially those who were severely disabled – were afraid that they would end up being 'done away with'. I had worked with people with severe disabilities, so I half-knew this already and hoped that ways could be found to reassure them. Now I realised that they were as difficult to reassure and to be converted to my way of thinking as I was to be reassured and converted myself. I also began to see that others, especially those who work in the caring professions and healers, wanted nothing to do with the purposeful ending of life, because it ran counter to everything they lived by. Again, I had half-known this, perhaps known it intellectually. Now I could appreciate the differences between us, and accept that no amount of reassurance, even the fact that they personally could be exempt from being involved in assisting a death, would change where they stood.

Towards the end of the evening, an elderly man stood up and asked if there was some way in which we could sense when the natural end of our life is near and allow it to happen, rather than resist it. His manner was warm and gruff; it was clear that the question came from a place deep within him. Members of the panel, who were from every sort of different viewpoint, looked at each other with a mixture of sadness and fellow-feeling, and I think I spoke for all of them when I said I was sorry, but the answer to his question was probably no.

This simple exchange brought to the front of my mind some powerful thoughts and feelings from the past and arranged them into a clear thread.

For many years I have had a dream, a sort of longing, for the awareness that the gruff old man at the debating society was asking for: that anyone could choose to die when they felt it right for them to do so.

During the seven years that I have been active in QDD, I have been asked to write articles for Quaker publications about our work. I sometimes agreed to do so, but found it difficult actually to sit down and write. Eventually I realised why: I could not write on behalf of the group, I had to do it in a personal way. In September 2013, the four short pieces that I had written as personal reflections arising from my experience of QDD were published in *the Friend*. This is an extract from one of them:

Is it possible to discern the point at which one's life is rightly over, and without resistance, let it happen? This way has been strong in some spiritual disciplines (there's a fine description of the willed death of Satish Kumar's mother in his autobiography[2]) but it is antithetical to the medical model we have in our current western culture.

I've known one Friend, a member of QDD, who took this path. She had both personal and political reasons for her stance. She had a phobia of hospitals, and she'd say to doctors, 'Why should my life be medically prolonged when children in poorer countries are dying of easily treatable diseases?' They couldn't believe she meant it, but she did. When her time came, she stayed at home, set her affairs in order, and gradually ate less and fewer types of food, until she took only a little rice, and then she died.

I have no idea whether I could follow my Friend down this path. She had a specific medical condition, and she'd persuaded her family and her doctors to co-operate with her way. I can't guarantee that these conditions would apply to me. I can only say that I would prefer the resources that would be needed to keep me alive through my 90s and beyond to be spent on the young. I would like to be released.

These ponderings led to the realisation that I would prefer not to give the responsibility for my dying to someone else, but to take responsibility for it myself.

[2]Kumar, S. (1992) *No Destination*, Cambridge: Green Books, pp.140-141.

But, I can hear you berating me, the whole point about creating a change in the law on assisted dying is that it is for those who *cannot* take responsibility for their own deaths. And at the moment, those who help them risk grave penalties, which only a change in the law can prevent.

That is true. But I believe that our attitude to our deaths can, as in the case of my QDD friend, affect the manner and timing of our death. We all know of those who have hung on to life until their dearest friend or relative had reached the bedside, and those who have faded away when they lose hold of the meaning of their life or hope for the future. Tony Nicklinson, the assisted dying campaigner, when his last appeal for help to end his life had failed, stopped eating and died from pneumonia within six days.

I think that an open discussion about willingness to die would be useful. The assisted dying debate has already started it, and organisations like Dying Matters and initiatives such as Death Cafés have helped. There is also a movement, the Society for Old Age Rational Suicide, which presents the case for what they call rational suicide (www.soars.org.uk).

> They say: After eight or nine decades, many people rightly
> decide that their lives have been fully lived, and now they
> have a life which, for them, has finally become too long.

Questions

I would now like to look briefly at some questions which are difficult to express, but which do need to be looked at, for they are part of this multiple and complex debate.

If the number of those living long years in nursing homes increases, as it surely will, we are faced with the issue of resources: resources in terms of money, and resources in terms of energy, commitment and affection. The last three are unquantifiable. But take financial resources. I am writing in the wake of the general election of May 2015, when it is clear that the political policy of austerity will continue well into the future. We are told we 'can't afford' adequate benefits for people with disabilities or people with large families; students must pay for their own tuition; young couples cannot afford to buy even a starter home. The pension rules have already been relaxed to allow people to 'blow' the pension pot that used to be dedicated to an annuity. What will happen to people who have spent their retirement savings in this way? Who will pay for their nursing home fees if they live to 90, 100 or beyond? As we usher in a further £12 billion cuts in public spending, where is the money going to come from to care for those who, like a Friend in my Meeting, lay semi-comatose for seven years before her death? And if that care is ring-fenced, who else's care is left inadequate?

I have heard it said that an open discussion on these questions would lead to elderly people feeling they are in the way, and might ask for their deaths to be brought forward because it would save their relatives having to care for them or paying for their care. So an atmosphere of fear would develop, and carers and relatives might become suspect. This is a very real possibility. But such an open discussion might also enable the issues to be faced realistically, rather than avoided as they often are at present.

There is also the issue of trust: particularly the question of trust in the political and legal systems and trust in doctors. In this country we have immense trust in the NHS and its staff, but we have ever-reducing trust in politicians and lawyers. People in other countries, who have lived under different regimes during the twentieth and early twenty-first centuries (think Nazi Germany, Soviet Russia, and China), may have no trust in their political and legal systems, and not much more trust in doctors. Even in this country, when we look at the stress on public services that will arise when the worst consequences of climate change kick in, can we be sure that we will trust a law that allows the medical profession to take part in ending people's lives?

One of the most publicised aspects of this debate is the journey that some people make to end their lives with Dignitas in Zurich. I have no direct experience of Dignitas, the establishment which provides locally legal and medically safe physician-assisted dying. However, there was an occasion when, as the contact for QDD, I was put in touch with a case where a Quaker who had recently been diagnosed with serious cancer wanted to go very quickly to Dignitas. The Friend's family were divided as to whether or not they would support the request, and one was opposed on religious grounds. I consulted with others in QDD, and we decided to offer a meeting for clearness. This took place and, as it was confidential, we heard no more. Sometime later I read a notice of the death of this Friend, and it had taken place at home. In the interval, I tried to imagine the feelings that this Friend and this family would have coped with. Did the experience of seeking clearness lead them to a better understanding of each other's wishes, or did the dispute fester, creating rancour and resentment? Did our Friend, having seen the distress of some family members, decide against the journey to Zurich, or did the death come more peacefully because the impulse had been mulled over together within a safe space? Or might the

Friend's wish to die have strengthened, and overcome or even sidelined the family's opposition to it?

Preparation

These thoughts take me back to the hope expressed at the beginning of this article: that preparation for our decline and dying be done, from as early in our life as we are able, and recapitulated until the moment that our death actually takes place.

How can we do this? We can make and revise our wills, and deposit them in places and with people (including a solicitor) where they are safe yet can be readily found after our death. We can do the same with the Power of Attorney: more complicated and perhaps costly, now that a Lasting Power of Attorney has replaced the Enduring one, but worth doing because it makes clear our wish about who would handle both our financial affairs and the decisions about our health care, and offers safeguards against abuse. We can talk with our family about our funeral wishes, and let the appropriate members of our Quaker Meeting know on the appropriate form.

Each of these tasks leads to discussion with members of various professions and, more importantly, with those we love and who love us. The most important task in terms of the assisted dying issue is that we write an Advance Decision. This specifies our wishes about medical intervention in what may be the last stages of our life. It involves filling in quite a simple form, signing it, getting it witnessed and countersigned by one's GP. She or he will want to discuss it with you, to make sure you are doing it under no pressure. Finally, it requires putting it into a safe place and maybe giving a copy to the same solicitor as holds the will.

I used the word 'simple' in that paragraph – but it is not that simple. I am in the process of renewing my Advance Decision, and for an array of reasons it is taking me an astonishingly long time. But I have started, so I will finish… In fact, the writing of this article has finally enabled me to complete the task.

The Advance Decision, as well as being helpful to us in enabling discussions with our nearest and dearest, is also useful to members of the medical profession. I shall never forget the relief on the face of the senior nurse at the nursing home where we took my father-in-law for the last days of his life, when we told her: 'He's got an Advance Directive' (as it was then called). My father-in-law had asked to be discharged from hospital to a nursing home even though he was very near death, and the nursing home staff may have feared they would be blamed if he died soon after being brought to them. With an Advance Directive/Decision in their file, they would know that the family had discussed it with the patient and were agreed that, should the death be imminent, no medical intervention should prevent it, and the family would not sue if the death came sooner rather than later.

If families and close friends have these discussions, there is also a chance that, in the face of the reality of death and loss, old quarrels can be mended and those vital words said: 'Thank you, I love you, I'm sorry', and 'goodbye'. Those who have overwhelming fears about facing their decline and their death might seek counselling. I am doing this myself by spending one day a year with someone who has trained as a 'soul midwife'.

So where am I now in relation to the issue of assisted dying? I shall maintain my membership of Dignity in Dying; I may write to my MP when the next draft bill is placed before Parliament; I will keep up to date with medical and social developments surrounding the issue. I will also keep an open mind and an open and hopefully loving ear to all shades of opinion and feelings around the issue. I may be open to a change of opinion on the actual issue of a change in the law. I cannot see that happening, but who knows.

Does this make me a wise old Quaker bird, or a shilly-shallying fence-sitter? Maybe a bit of both.

The Quaker Concern around Dying and Death is perhaps the antithesis of a campaigning group. It is a place where any view can be articulated and any change of mind, or new and unusual insight, can be set alongside the more traditional insights of the group or of the Religious Society of Friends as a whole. As QDD has developed, it has become more than a single-focus organisation; it is one where it is safe to ask awkward questions, and work through possible answers or sit with the discomfort of there being no clear answer. That ethos was one of the many reasons why I joined the Religious Society of Friends nearly fifty years ago, and I think it is the ethos underlying the publication of this volume.

I hope that the traditional Quaker practices of threshing, listening, discernment, and thinking it possible that we may be mistaken, will be central to the process. I offer this article in the spirit of our *Advices and Queries* (15)

> Do you consider difficult questions with an informed mind
> as well as a generous and loving spirit? Are you prepared
> to let your insights and personal wishes take their place
> alongside those of others or be set aside?

Occasionally, at the back of my mind, there comes a little voice saying: 'But are you not trying to control something which is, essentially, beyond your control?' And another voice answers back, 'Yes – and why not?' And the original voice says firmly, 'You can't control death'. This is an ongoing drama. Even if the law is changed, the drama will go on.

Palliative physicians – why are we so uneasy about assisted dying?

Rosemary Daley

Assisted dying is a subject that raises much emotion, and I find entering the debate quite nerve-wracking. It is easy for the discussion to become polarised and angry so that listening and discernment get lost. But I have some particular experiences that make me feel I have something to offer in this debate. So here is my tentative offering.

I have been a doctor working in palliative medicine for nearly thirty years. I retired three years ago but I still do some strategic work nationally, trying to get good palliative care available for anyone who is dying at any age of any disease. By which I mean that I campaign for education and services that enable professionals to help patients who will die in the next few months to plan and get medical care in the way they want; that they can then get the symptom control and the caring and compassionate nursing that they need, in the place they want if at all possible; and also any emotional support that they want or need. I am passionate about this effort.

I have also had fairly high risk breast cancer, about twelve years ago. I had a mastectomy and chemotherapy and radiotherapy, and I think now I can probably say that I am free of the disease, though it could still come back.

So how do these two sets of experiences affect my thinking about dying and death? I went into palliative medicine because I felt that care of the dying was the most worthwhile part of medicine I could find and, at the time, one of the most challenging, as there was little research or medical wisdom on how to do it. It gave me a hugely rewarding career, but it also meant that I became accustomed to death in a way that I realise sets me apart from most people. I suppose I must indirectly and directly have looked after thousands of people who have died, and have been close to about thirty a year – these usually because they had difficult symptoms or particular difficulty in coping with dying. By close, I mean that I saw them weekly or more often, and that we would talk intimately about how they were feeling physically and emotionally and sometimes spiritually. Some few became friends.

I hope that the personality and strength of so many of the dying people whom I have accompanied on their journey towards dying, and the intimacy of some of these relationships, have protected me from thinking arrogantly that I have all (or any of) the answers about death and dying. But I know that this experience of death on a daily basis has given me an unusual familiarity with dying. I really do see it as part of the natural life-cycle, and I guess I think of death as accompanying me through life as a companion and teacher in rather the way of the illustrations of the medieval texts on good death and dying (the *Ars Moriendi*). I am continually, sometimes uncomfortably, aware of the fragility of our lives and of the need always to live life to the full in the present moment. I guess it has made me try to do what I really wanted or felt was right in life and not to defer too many things to a future when there is 'more time'. I retired a bit early for this reason.

Because of this experience and that of my own cancer, I have thought about and planned for my own death. I have an up-to-date will. If I was dying I hope I would be able to find a way to live the time I had left fruitfully and with grace and to die as naturally as possible. But I have written clear accounts of how I would wish to be treated in various circumstances if I was unable to communicate at the time, and of the principles behind those wishes that I would wish to be used in any unforeseen illness or accident[1]. I have particularly stressed some circumstances when I would not wish for any medical treatment at all, but would want to be made comfortable and allowed to die.

There are a few illnesses that scare me particularly and I wonder whether I would want to kill myself if I got them. I am not against suicide, but I am horribly aware of the pain it can cause those left behind. I have had about six patients in my career who have definitely committed suicide (which seems surprisingly few to me given the drugs most patients have available); and about another five where I have suspected it but not been sure. I can only remember one failed suicide attempt.

Legalisation

However, I am quite uneasy about the legalisation of assisted dying, while feeling it would benefit some individuals. I am not against it 'morally' – but I am not alone among palliative doctors in my unease. In a recent survey of palliative physicians on Lord Falconer's Assisted Dying Bill there were 82% definitely against and only 12% for it; 73% thought assisted suicide would have an adverse or very adverse effect on palliative care; only 4% would be

---

[1] http://www.nhs.uk/Planners/end-of-life-care/Pages/why-plan-ahead.aspx or http://www.alzheimers.org.uk search documentID=143

prepared to participate fully in its implementation.[2] So why are we tending to be against assisted dying, and so reluctant to have anything to do with it?

I thought it might be useful to summarise the reasons usually discussed, not didactically but rather to flesh out some of them a little, and to try to understand how the experience of caring for the dying and having a life-threatening illness myself has shaped my views.

I do not know any colleagues who put the straight moral argument first, but there is a feeling that it is a big step to actually, proactively, take a life. Palliative physicians are used to not prolonging medical treatments if they are not in the long-term interests of a patient; we are generally so aware of the importance of quality of life that we really like discussing benefits and burdens of treatments to see if they should be withdrawn; we are happy to let nature take its course and keep people comfortable through the decline and dying process without feeling the need to treat everything (like a chest infection) if someone does not want it treating; we are used to using drugs to give good symptom control even if they might have side effects which would shorten someone's life.

But actually killing people (or handing them the means to kill themselves) does *feel* different. Is it perhaps it is so ingrained in us

[2] Association for Palliative Medicine – survey Jan 2015 of 387 doctors: http://217.199.187.67/apmonline.org/wp-content/uploads/2015/05/APM-survey-on-Assisted-Suicide-website.pdf. For the Association of Palliative Medicine's official statement on assisted dying see: http://apmonline.org/wp-content/uploads/2015/07/AS-Full-briefing-final.pdf

that our craft is to heal people? Is it perhaps to control the moment of death just feels a step too near to playing God?

Perhaps it just feels it disturbs the trust in the doctor-patient relationship. I am not sure. If we go a step further and consider what effect legalising assisted dying would have on society's views on suicide, around death or at other times, it gets more difficult still. Some people have called the basic principle that we do not involve ourselves in deliberately bringing about the deaths of other people 'a bright line'[3] [4] which keeps us safe. I have tried to think this through. I am sure that it is true that changes in the law would change attitudes in society to suicide generally and to the idea of euthanasia. Laws do change views – our attitude to abortion has changed hugely since 1967 when it was legalised. I am not saying that abortion is wrong, just that it was considered a last resort when the Bill was introduced, and is now considered a routine procedure and by some as a method of contraception. How would it affect the ill, depressed or disabled if suicide in terminal illness is officially sanctioned, and if doctors provide the means? It is reported that where euthanasia is allowed (if not legal) then the numbers using it are growing and the reasons for using it are sometimes widening beyond terminal illness.

[3] Lady Colin Campbell on Lord Falconer's bill 2014:
http://www.telegraph.co.uk/news/uknews/law-and-order/10717279/Disabled-peer-Lord-Falconers-assisted-suicide-plans-send-shiver-down-my-spine.html
[4]Baroness Butler-Sloss:
http://www.telegraph.co.uk/news/health/elder/10517890/We-legalise-assisted-dying-at-our-peril.html

When I listen to debates about euthanasia and assisted dying, everyone always seems so clear in their arguments, and they suggest that people with terminal illnesses who want assisted dying are equally clear and consistent in their wishes. But that is not how it has seemed to me in real life.

I used to think that the idea that people changed their mind about euthanasia with good care was a rather sickly story emanating from the hospice movement. But then I found that they really did – I remember one man begging me to kill him; two weeks later in outpatients with better pain relief and having gone home, he was saying 'I was wrong. My wife still needs me. I have things to do'. And he had initially made me feel really regretful and guilty that I could not do what he had wanted. If he had the means earlier, and it was legally and socially acceptable, I am sure he would have done it. This does not make assisted dying wrong, but I think it does complicate the matter. If I am ill, or in pain, I think differently from when I am comfortable. Sometimes I want to feel full of energy; at other times I can enjoy feeling tired and just relax into it. Sometimes I hate the idea of being cared for by others; sometimes I value frailty and don't mind the idea of others caring for my needs. My own feelings certainly change with time. Sometimes I feel strong and able to make decisions for myself; at other times I feel I would need help to do what I think is right. I remember one youngish woman saying to me: 'No, I don't want antibiotics if I get a chest infection. But don't ask me at the time – I would have to say yes to them, if you asked me'.[5] People are complicated. I have looked after a few

[5]See also Andrew Lloyd Webber on how one's views can change with time and circumstance:
http://www.telegraph.co.uk/news/politics/10974783/Lloyd-Webber-I-considered-Dignitas-but-am-set-to-oppose-assisted-dying.html

people who were really articulate and clear that they thought assisted suicide should be available to them, and that they would kill themselves now if they could, and they did not waver in that view. But they all had drugs at home with them which would have killed them in only a small overdose; they knew these were dangerous drugs – the bottles say so clearly; they had the intelligence, the means and the ability to end their lives. But they did not do so. I do not know why. I do not know why there are not lots of overdose suicides among the terminally ill. I can only think that people go on finding life worth something; or that they need it to be approved by formal legislation before they are comfortable to do it; or that in the end, it feels right to let oneself go naturally, not to try to be in control after all. I have known one or two who campaigned for assisted dying until they died, and it almost seemed to me as if having such a cause to campaign for was what kept them alive. I say again: people are complicated.

Society confuses me at the moment in the way we talk about death and dying. It is good that we are talking about it, but we seem to be in a state of flux and confusion culturally about how we want to manage dying. On the one hand, we have strong advocates of euthanasia and assisted dying with very convincing arguments delivered with energy, persistence and passion. On the other hand, we have the people horrified that doctors might be shortening life by a few days with the Liverpool Care Pathway (LCP) for the dying – which was honestly just a tool to help professionals look after people well in their last few days. I thought it was useful; the professionals using it did need to understand the principles of care at lay behind it, but this meant you could use it as a vehicle for education in hospitals and in community services. The force of the campaign against this pathway was extraordinary and led ultimately to its withdrawal, and made many doctors and nurses much less confident about using drugs for comfort at the end of life. I completely accept that there were stories of the LCP being misused – any tool can be used badly – but these seemed to me to be few beside the very large numbers of cases where it was used well. There seemed to be a tremendous fear that it was being used to save money and to free up beds and to kill people before their time. People still refer to it with fear in hospitals and hospices and worry that their death will be hastened by doctors.

My point is not about the LCP but about the confusion in society about death and dying. We have not talked about what a 'good death' can or could be. Only a third of people have made a Will when they die. Very few seem to write down their wishes about dying in ways which really do help doctors and nurses to carry out the right care for them. We give as individuals with great generosity to hospices, but our governments do not fund health or care services well enough to ensure that all those who have life- shortening illnesses can die comfortably and with dignity. I worry about passing any sort of law about assisted dying under these confused conditions. And I worry that the emphasis on the campaign for assisted dying distracts from the campaign for the provision of good care for the dying and the need for us generally to prepare well for our own deaths.

Relational beings

One of the main arguments in favour of assisted dying is the right of the individual to control their own life and death. For many people this principle of the autonomy of the individual is very strong and trumps other ethical principles. It actually defines much of the law around medical treatment already because we live in a society that values autonomy highly. Any mentally competent person can refuse a treatment even if all the professionals think the treatment would help them, and can define to whom doctors give information about them. Relatives' wishes have no weight legally in these decisions – although relatives and close friends must be consulted about what the ill person would want if that person cannot communicate their wishes at the time.

The trouble is that I do not really think humans are autonomous in this way. Humans are 'relational' beings. When I had breast cancer and had to decide whether to have all the treatments on offer, including six months of chemotherapy which would only improve my chances of living by 8%, I felt about as autonomous as a lemming. I had young children; I come from a large family, some of whom were medical, and all of whom were upset; most of my family and friends wanted me to do everything possible. To go against the doctors' best offers was, in effect, impossible for me to contemplate. I am not grumbling about this, just saying that I did not feel autonomous and that is what my experience tells me it is like for most people. Few people live as islands. I certainly do not and in the end my decisions rest as much on what the people I love think is right as on my own feelings.

We relate not only to our family and friends, but also to the society we live in. If we legalise assisted suicide, then we will alter the culture within our society about what is the most sensible, responsible and admirable way to live until we die. This will then inevitably affect how people decide to manage their terminal illnesses. Recognising the power of cultural opinion, Lord Walton said of his committee's discussions in the 1994 debates on euthanasia, 'we were also concerned that vulnerable people – the elderly, lonely, sick or distressed – would feel pressure, whether real or imagined, to request early death'.[6] The British Geriatric Society shares this view being 'concerned with protecting the interests of vulnerable older and disabled people who already feel pressure to give up their lives to reduce the burden they feel they cause to others.'

I worked in poor areas for most of my working life. Many of the ill people I came to know fit this description of vulnerability and many made it a priority 'not to be a nuisance'. But I think often they enjoyed their last months even if frail and not able to follow all their old pleasures. Many told me that life was still sweet. And I am sure some of them would have chosen to die earlier if it had been a readily acceptable option, but not really for their own sakes.

And then there is the financial case, because it would be much cheaper if people who were going to die, died quickly. About 20% of the NHS costs goes on care of those in the last year of life. The NHS budget is stretched and the care budget is even more inadequate and not ring-fenced. I hate the thought that once it is legal to speed up dying, then it will become less necessary to fund good care for the end of life. Unfortunately, I can imagine a time when only the rich could afford to live for long after a terminal diagnosis because only they could buy good care; and when it would

[6] Lord Walton: Hansard, May 9th 1994, House of Commons Official Report.

be considered irresponsible and selfish to ask for this care from limited budgets which could be used on fitter, younger people.

The value of a frail life

There is a counterpoint to the value we place on autonomy. As a society, I do not think we generally place much value on interdependence. We think disability, frailty and vulnerability hugely reduce our quality of life. We, or at least our governments, fund medical and care services as if frail or disabled people had less value than independent and productive people. Those who advocate the legalising of assisted dying usually say in surveys that it is the loss of independence and dignity that they fear, or being a burden on others. Legalising the shortening of life would inevitably reinforce this trend in our thinking. I do not want this trend to go further. I would like to see us begin to realise the value of both giving and receiving help; the value of the last phase of our life even if we are feeble, when we can talk to our friends and family – apologise, celebrate, pass on our fears and our wisdom.

My own father had a rather late diagnosis of cancer of the pancreas after many months of pain. When he was finally diagnosed, we were all worn out and terribly sad. I think that if assisted suicide had been available we would have had to choose it and think that it was for the best after all his suffering. In the event, he got good pain control finally and his last two months were like a blessing after the previous six. He was comfortable and could eat a little and enjoy eating. I know that he had a chance to speak or write to some family members to reassure and comfort them. I looked after him for one weekend when my mother was away and I value enormously what we talked about and the peaceful time we had together.

It is a fine line. My father did not want to prolong his life and he did not go into hospital when he was actually dying in case they tried to resuscitate him. And I know that if I or anyone in my family was demented I would feel that it was good not to have any life-extending treatments such as artificial feeding. I tend to feel that being able to refuse treatments is probably enough; we would not need assisted dying or euthanasia legislation if doctors and nurses were rigorous about properly discussing treatments with their patients. The two key elements of this would be, firstly, finding out what sort of life is acceptable to each of them and what burdensome treatments they would or would not be willing to have to try to extend their life; secondly, if, before they became ill, everyone were prepared to think about these issues and to write down their views for future reference.

Conclusion

What, then, am I really asking? I think I want us to start from the position that assisted dying is a difficult and complicated matter and that we need to understand how we and the rest of society are thinking and feeling about death and dying generally before we change the law. I wonder if we should start by discussing death more ourselves and thinking what a good death means to us and why. As part of this discussion we could look again at *Advices and Queries* (30) which seems to me to be impressive:

> Are you able to contemplate your death and the death of those closest to you? Accepting the fact of death, we are freed to live more fully.

On a practical level, based on my professional experience, I would like us to encourage and help people to give their views on a good death to their friends and family and their GPs so as to avoid the sort of treatments they do not want. We could ask the government to fund more education and time for all doctors and nurses around holistic care in the last year of life. Then we could agitate to fund medical and nursing care and palliative care at the end of life properly, and even organise and enable volunteers to help with support and care so that people knew that they were not useless or burdensome in their frailty. And if we did all that, then I think I might stop being so uneasy about legalising assisted dying for those who want it.

A Quaker doctor's view on end-of-life care

Martin Schweiger

There are some core responsibilities for all doctors. For those practising in Britain the responsibilities are either formally set out by the General Medical Council (GMC) or are embedded in the general professional ethos. Peer review, annual appraisals and continued professional education all help to sustain the bounds of acceptable professional behaviour. Hippocrates is credited with the first rule of medicine which is simply stated as 'First do no harm'. That is as true today as when it was when first stated. Doing no harm is at the heart of the issues posed by the dying patient who asks for help in bringing forward his or her death. The nature of the harm that is done in meeting, deflecting or denying the request is a genuine dilemma, varying with each request.

Meeting the GMC's direction to make the patient's best interests my primary concern assumes that I know what my patient's best interests really are. Trying to determine my own best interests can be a challenge at times, so knowing the best interests for someone who, perhaps, I have only met within the confines of a professional relationship, for a limited period of time, is not easy. Perspective is critical but inevitably changes over time with experience of events and the accumulation of knowledge. The information I have about a patient may so easily be wrong, not because anyone sets out to deceive but because of limits to human communication.

My membership of the Society of Friends influences my view that all of life is sacred. For me that means there is always a blurring of the lines between what I do as an individual, as a member of a family, as a public health consultant for the last thirty years and as a

Quaker. They all influence each other, making me the person that I am and influencing all my relationships with other people. The quality of the relationship seems to me to be particularly critical with people coming to the end of their lives.

Relationships

If a good relationship is established between patient and doctor, there is a therapeutic benefit that goes beyond what will be achieved by clinical treatment alone. Mutual respect and trust are essential but are difficult, within the constraints of time-limited appointments, to establish. Aligning expectations is not always straightforward either as there is a general presumption that the patient has only a limited number of problems and that the doctor can cure them. For the dying patient the problems are rarely boxed into a defined number of neat parcels to be presented in order of priority.

Knowledge that the patient is dying immediately puts the expectation of cure beyond the doctor's reach. Knowledge that a patient is dying may be wrong; I have been greeted in the street by a man whom I had advised about his impending death ten years earlier. However, the expectation that a patient is dying brings us to a point where it becomes easy to put a distance into the relationship between doctor and patient. At worst, the patient is seen as a bed-blocker or as someone to be ignored because there is nothing to be gained from attending to them; they only demonstrate my failure to cure. Acceptance that the relationship is imperfect does not prevent it being workable, but it does require continual attention. Alongside the doctor-patient relationship are the multiple other relationships between family and friends around the dying patient and the clinical care team.

Evidence of expertise often comes in knowing boundaries. Doctors who know everything are almost certainly mistaken and probably deceiving themselves more than their patients. Why should we expect that the family doctor, the doctor we know best, has expertise in end-of-life care and in assisting patients to terminate their life at the time of their choosing? It is reasonable to expect that the doctor we know best will refer patients wishing to discuss how their life can be ended in the manner of their choosing to someone with expertise in that area, but who will inevitably know the patient less well. For a life-critical decision is it better to accept that we have to take advice from strangers rather than from a familiar figure who has less of the relevant expertise? Confidence and trust arise naturally in long-term relationships.

Doctors who take on the burden of supporting patients making decisions about end-of-life care, which may one day include bringing an end to that life, must have skills in relationship-building based on a combination of deep expertise and empathy. Care at the end of life requires attention to pain and physical problems as well as any mental distress. The social aspects of death are at least as complex as the physical and mental issues. Legal issues are currently a major concern, not the least of which is that assisting suicide is currently illegal. There are so many diverse issues to consider that the expertise almost certainly has to come from an expert team so that patient, informal carers and relatives do not feel rushed. Bringing a pattern, creating harmony is important because without them any attempt to bring dignity to the dying will be in vain.

Ethical issues are never far away in medical care. Whatever a doctor does will be criticised. The starting point is knowing that you will get it wrong, so what is the least worst option? A sense of values helps the doctor to determine the least worst option. For Quakers the starting point is the recognition of that of God within both the patient and oneself. The Peace Testimony encourages us to bear witness to a rejection of violence and harm to all people. Assisting suicide or killing a patient is certainly an act of irreversible harm to another living being. I can be seen to uphold the Peace Testimony by rejecting any involvement in assisted suicide. On the other hand do I really uphold Quaker values by walking past on the other side, saying that assisted suicide is simply wrong and the patient's distress is merely the price of my doing the right thing?

It is a great help that for many patients much can be done to relieve suffering and distress. Progress made in palliative care in recent years has been wonderful, so the need for requests to terminate life may one day be completely removed. Likewise, evidence from Belgium has shown that many patients draw strength from knowing that if life does become unbearable they can request that their lives be ended. Experience in Belgium (see appendix) has demonstrated that few patients actually make that request.

Any consideration of end-of-life care brings the reminder that one day all of us will die. Different perspectives bring different ideas; is it the end of all that we know or the beginning of a whole new experience? There are experiences I personally never wish to have and I can sympathise with those who wish to avoid such experiences or bring them to an end by whatever means are available to our patients. Health care is advancing all the time and what was not possible has now become almost routine. How well currently available treatments deal with pain, distress, disability, loss of dignity, disempowerment and depression is a complete spectrum and there is a wide range of responses from individuals as to what is acceptable to them. For the doctor there is an obligation to do one's utmost to find effective palliation and to make it available. If death is the only way of achieving the level of palliation sought by the patient, health care professionals are in a real dilemma.

Medical murders

In living, do we bring something positive into the lives of those around us? In dying, do we seek escape from hardships and difficulties? If, as a doctor, I seek to assist a patient to die does that give me a sense of power over life and death, almost certainly a factor in the murders committed by Harold Shipman (during the 1980s and 1990s), and other medical murderers? Harold Shipman compounded his murders by seeking financial gain from some of them. If I assist a patient to die I need to take great care that I do not gain pecuniary or other advantage from my actions. That places private practitioners in difficulties to distinguish between a fee for a professional service and profiting from a patient's death. In the last year of life people tend to make more demands on health services than in their previous years of living; helping someone to die may decrease the burden of providing those services. If I have been called on to provide much of the medical support required, is my involvement in bringing that life to an end simply a way of easing the pressures on me and my colleagues?

However we proceed and whatever the law may or may not permit, there is an inherent safeguard in working with a team. The more expert the team is across the whole range of palliative care the greater the choices for care. Options include reviewing over time and accepting that what is right today may no longer be right next week. Getting it as right as possible for today really matters; we can think again in the morning; focus on making living worthwhile and positive even if it is not easy; think of enjoying the sunrise rather than despairing at the coming of the dark at nightfall. As a junior doctor I was advised that critical decisions and actions should not be taken in the dark. My experience tells me that this is true; decisions are better if made when there is light in the sky and spiritual light comes into the decision-making. Life for those who live on after the death of a loved one begins better when awake in daylight than when trying to sleep in the dark.

I am no expert in palliative care. As a public health professional I am not likely to be called upon to advise anyone about end-of-life care or physician-assisted suicide. As a public health physician I need to think across the whole population, which includes all patients and health professionals with frequent reminders that doctors can become patients too. We need to recognise diversity; there is no single way forward. What is right for one patient will not be right, at any one time, for another. Developing helpful choices and providing menus of options for both patient and the health care team make good sense to me. I would certainly like to see the law modified to enable choices to be made with reasonable safeguards in place for patients, families and health care professionals. It seems to me that empowering patients to make informed choices is the right way forward.

The GMC sets expectations and boundaries for my decisions and actions. However, there are other strong influences arising from my personal value system, experiences and the relationships I enjoy with those around me. My professional competence is always going to be limited by my knowledge, training and the sheer diversity of human conditions. In complex and difficult areas such as providing the appropriate care for a dying patient, working with others –

professionals, the family and of course the patient – make appropriate decisions more likely. As a public health physician I can advocate for evidence-based, humane options to be both professionally and legally supported. For the doctor and other health care professionals involved we can recognise our own limitations and then hold out our hand to accompany our patients whichever way they choose to go.

Disability and assisted dying

Tom Shakespeare

In thinking about assisted dying, my starting point is the values of the disability rights movement. One in seven of the population is disabled in some way, even though a tiny minority is actively involved in disability politics. So I will begin by outlining some of the values of the disability movement. To begin with, disabled people argue strongly that disabled lives have value. Disabled people can contribute to society. Through their relationships with others and in many other ways they lead good lives that should be supported and celebrated. This is a radical claim. Rather than achievements or qualifications or salaries or status, disabled people want to be regarded as people in their own right, as worthy of respect and dignity. This ethic is very close to the Quaker ethic of looking for that of God in everyone.

As an aside, I wish that the politics of disability could be more inspiring for the politics of old age. There has not yet been an equivalent older people's movement alongside the disabled people's movement, and many older people have been unpersuaded by disability rights thinking. Yet the refusal to be subject to medical domination, the determination to achieve choice and control, the demand for inclusion and respect, are all relevant to older people, with and without disability, and they could be influential in the debate on assisted dying. It is very encouraging to see that advocates are beginning to develop a disability-inspired human rights approach to dementia, for example.

It is not always easy for people with impairments or illnesses to recognise themselves as disabled people and feel pride and self-worth. Many children with disabilities are brought up to feel second class, to feel dependent, and to be grateful for any help they can get. Many people who develop disability in adulthood – perhaps through sudden injury or acquired disease – take time to adapt and accommodate. The initial reaction to traumatic or acquired disability is dismay. People often feel suicidal – I know I did, when I became spinal cord injured.

First, it is hard to get used to not being able to do things that previously were taken for granted. Yet the evidence shows that people do adapt, and do come to terms. Although subjective quality of life plummets on becoming impaired, within a very few years, it returns to what it was before. Sometimes, post-disability quality of life is not only better than what came before, but better than that of non-disabled people. This is counter-intuitive, extraordinary even. But it is true, with some rare exceptions. This concept is known as 'hedonic adaptation', and is a very heartening example of how good human beings are at coming to terms with life changes.

Second, disabled people have argued for their human rights to be recognised and have demanded services and inclusion on the basis of these rights. The 2006 UN Convention on the Rights of Persons with Disabilities enshrines these rights. More than 150 states, including the United Kingdom, have ratified this Convention and are therefore bound to respect and promote these rights. The Convention is predicated on the radical idea that people are disabled by society as much as by their bodies. That is why concepts such as equality and discrimination, access and attitudes are highlighted in the first few Articles. It is often the barriers that are put in the way of disabled people which prevent them leading good lives or being included in education, employment, housing or leisure opportunities.

Central to these human rights is the principle of 'nothing about us without us', the principle that disabled people should be listened to and regarded as the experts on their own lives. Disabled people have argued strongly for choice and control over their own lives. Historically, disabled people have been spoken for by others. They have been passive recipients of care. Non-disabled people have often been motivated by pity. As a result, disabled people have lacked dignity and autonomy. That is why the principles of independent living have been so important. Even when people are severely impaired, they can be provided with their own personal assistants. This means that they can live independently in their own homes, participating in the community. These principles have now been eroded by 'welfare reform', and many disabled people fear being returned to the residential institutions from which they escaped in the 1970s and 1980s.

Third, disabled people also remember their history of eugenics and euthanasia. Not just in Nazi Germany, but in all of Scandinavia and many parts of the United States and Canada, disabled people were sterilised, particularly those labelled as 'feeble-minded'. Under the Third Reich, this hatred of 'useless eaters' or 'lives unworthy of life' went as far as active euthanasia, with several hundred thousand children and adults with mental health conditions or intellectual disabilities being exterminated in gas chambers, by lethal injection, by machine gun or by neglect. So disabled people have experience of being treated in an evil way by society, with doctors as the agents of their discriminatory treatment.

These competing principles influence disabled people's attitudes to assisted dying in different ways. Some disabled people are adamantly opposed to any liberalisation of the law. They cite the history of eugenics and involuntary euthanasia, fearing that even a narrow and restrictive liberalisation will be the first step on a slippery slope. They highlight how the majority of the population has at best patronising, and at worst eugenic, attitudes to disability. They make the point that people newly disabled will share these negative valuations, and will feel that their own lives are not worth living. They fear that disabled people will feel pressurised by other family members to end their own lives, without exploring the possibilities of independent living, personal assistance and lives supported by assisted technology. After all, thousands of disabled people are living good lives, despite relying on machines to breathe, or assistants to bathe and feed them.

Yet other disabled people point to the disability rights movement's value of choice and control. If we campaign for independent lives, should we not also campaign for autonomy at the end of life? Rather than having a difficult, lingering death, why not decide for oneself when enough is enough? If we believe that disabled people can decide for themselves, why can they not be permitted to decide about this most important question?

Terminal illness

Central to a disability rights support for assisted dying is a differentiation between people living with disability, and people in the end stage of terminal illness. It seems to me that it would be very wrong for any person who is disabled automatically to have the right to die. Death is not the answer to disability. When I hear of a young

68

man who has become spinal cord injured travelling to Zurich to die in the Dignitas scheme, I feel very sad. This is because, as I mentioned above, the evidence is that disabled people can have a quality of life as good as non-disabled people, and sometimes even better.

However, where someone is already dying, with a disease such as motor neurone disease or terminal cancer, it seems irrational to deny to them the right of a better death. The outcome is not changed: they would be dead within months anyway. They are not giving up on the possibilities of a long and fulfilled life, because they might have less than a year to live. Independent living is barely relevant, because no amount of accessibility or support services can compensate when one is struggling to breathe, or eat, or else enduring constant pain. The Quaker principle of equality is appropriate: if a healthy person wanted to end their life through suicide, they would be able to perform that act. But this terminally ill person, living at home or in hospital in a state of complete debility, is highly unlikely to be able to end their own life. Hence the need for assistance.

The counter-argument from colleagues like Jane Campbell, the disability rights campaigner, is that sometimes disabled people already have a terminal diagnosis: they are not expected to survive spinal muscular atrophy (SMA) or muscular dystrophy (MD) or multiple sclerosis (MS) in the long term. If they have a sudden crisis, perhaps pneumonia, they may be thought of as being in the end stage of their disease. 'Do Not Attempt Resuscitation' (DNAR or DNR) may be placed on their hospital notes. So the two categories, of disabled people living independent lives, and terminally ill people experiencing a slow death, are sometimes hard to differentiate. Yet I come back to the principle of autonomy.

69

Assisted dying should never be something that is imposed on someone. It should be something that is chosen by someone who knows that life is futile because they are inevitably going to die in weeks or days. This does not apply to people with SMA or MD or MS.

I strongly favour people having conversations about death with their loved ones. The Death Café movement is a good example of this. As our *Advices and Queries* suggest, 'Accepting the fact of death, we are freed to live more fully' (number 30). We should know what our partners, parents and siblings want to do at the end of life: whether they want to be organ donors or not; whether assisted dying is in line with their values, or not; what sort of treatment they would want to receive. Of course, people fear disability, almost as much as they fear dying. People may say they would rather be dead than endure dependency, but then when dependency happens, they discover that it is not the worst way to live, and that life can have value. That is why it is important to go on having those conversations, and to hear from the person directly affected about what is good and bad about their existence. That is why I also support the idea of Advance Decisions, which allow someone to say what they wish to happen to them in future, if they are unable to decide for themselves.

Very few people will wish to avail themselves of assisted dying, based on the evidence from Oregon. In 2014, there were 31 assisted deaths per 10,000 deaths (a total of 105 people in Oregon). So after 15 years of the legislation, the number of people who took advantage of it represented less than one per cent (0.31%) of all deaths. But many more will have been given extra courage in facing death by the knowledge that there is an easier way out, if they wish to take it.

I do not think that this threatens disabled people, as long as safeguards are in place. The analysis of effects of the legislation in Oregon and the Netherlands is that vulnerable groups – such as disabled people, older people, women, poorer people and people with histories of psychiatric illness – are not unfairly affected (Battin et al., 2007). From Oregon, we also know that the median age of people who chose assisted dying in 2014 was 72: 69% had cancer, 16% had motor neurone disease, 93% were enrolled in hospice care. So these are not young disabled people being victims of euthanasia, they are dying people, who have access to good services, who decide that they want choice at the end of life. These individuals were also asked what influenced their decisions to ask for assisted dying. The three most cited concerns at end of their life were: loss of autonomy (91%); decreasing ability to participate in activities that made life enjoyable (87%); loss of dignity (71%).

You could say that all disabled people face these factors. But I think there is a difference between the experience faced by dying people, and the experience of disabled people. The latter group can employ their own personal assistants, participate in society, and not allow their physical limitations to define them. But in my experience of being with friends who are dying, these are not their goals or ambitions. They have had plenty of support from partners and friends. But their activities have been steadily circumscribed, pain has increased, and body functions have been failing. I remember one dear friend, dying of advanced metastatic cancer in her late forties, lying on a hospital bed, doubled up, yellow with jaundice, and in extreme discomfort. I was glad to have the chance to say goodbye, and it was clear to me that none of what I could offer as a disabled activist was at all relevant to her needs at that moment: all she required was loving kindness.

Views of disabled people

What do disabled people think about assisted dying? In my experience, most disability rights activists are adamantly opposed to the liberalisation of the law. Vocal among them have sometimes been religious people – Catholics like Alison Davis, who was severely disabled and who was strongly opposed to both abortion and assisted dying. Inside and outside Parliament, disability rights arguments have been used by religious opponents of the law, and disability activists have lined up next to 'pro-life' banner-wavers.

Yet on this topic, like some others, disability rights leaders are not in tune with the majority of disabled people. Dignity in Dying commissioned a poll from Populus in 2015 which found that 86% of people with a disability supported the Assisted Dying Bill. A similar poll by YouGov in 2013 found that 80% of disabled people supported assisted dying. There have been polls showing concern among disabled people about assisted dying legislation, for example, one commissioned by Scope in 2014, but other data suggests that disabled people have similar views to non-disabled people and support liberalisation. Similarly, two Australian research studies with people with cancer found the majority supporting assisted dying type proposals (Eliott and Olver, 2008; Parkinson et al. 2005). Yet disabled people's organisations have vehemently opposed assisted dying, and the rare individuals such as myself who are prepared to go on record as supporting these legislative proposals are attacked, sometimes on a very personal basis. I think disabled people's organisations should be neutral on assisted dying. They should outline the arguments and evidence on both sides, so that disabled people are empowered to express their own, well-informed, views.

Clearly, there is considerable fear among some activists. But, as with some of the fears around hate crime, I believe this is out of proportion. I am not complacent, but I want to believe the best of people. I think that in the medical profession there is a very strong commitment to keeping people alive. In general, doctors have opposed assisted dying (McCormack et al., 2011), perhaps because to them it is an admission of defeat, an acceptance that medicine has its limits. Other prominent medical spokespeople, such as Baroness Ilora Finlay, have opposed assisted dying; I think this is because they have a strong commitment to palliative care and believe that it can always make dying bearable. So I do not fear doctors. I do not think that a few very rare cases such as Shipman have any implications for the medical profession as a whole, except to reinforce the importance of vigilance.

Similarly, disabled people sometimes fear that family members will wish them speedily dead. They fear that relatives will have one beady eye on their financial resources. They predict that terminally ill people will be pressured to opt for assisted dying. Again, I do not think this is very plausible. I also think that the safeguards in the proposed legislation – having to petition two doctors and one judge – are strong enough to eliminate cases where a dying person is operating under duress. Already, NHS patients have the right to refuse treatment. So if a person is dependent on oxygen or other life support, they can request that this be turned off. Patients can refuse hydration and nutrition, so if they are courageous enough to choose to die from lack of water or food, they can slowly fade away. Yet I have not seen any evidence that any people in these situations are put under pressure to die by family members or doctors.

Opponents also fear the so-called 'slippery slope'. They argue that if you relax the law in the very limited situation of terminal illness, pressure will follow to allow any disabled person access to assisted dying and, following that, to allow any person whatsoever to access assisted dying. Needless to say, I would oppose both those measures, as would the vast majority of the population. No doubt, some euthanasia zealots would still press for further liberalisation, but they would be a tiny minority. Laws are often a compromise. An example is abortion. Some people would favour abortion on demand; others would favour a complete ban. Instead, we have a reasonable measure which sets a limit of viability of twenty-four weeks, and says that only in the most exceptional circumstances can abortion be permitted after this deadline. This seems a settled position, and it appears unlikely at the moment that abortion law will change (this does not mean that the law is not sometimes abused, which is of course wrong). The fact that a law is a compromise does not mean that it will inevitably slide into permissiveness. At each stage, there is a debate, reasons and evidence are provided, and society and Parliament decide. Despite what some more extreme opponents occasionally say, we are not living in a Nazi euthanasia scenario and, in a democratic society, have no prospect of being there. We live in a world where there is prejudice, admittedly, but there is also increasing acceptance and support, and considerable sympathy, for disabled people.

Opponents of liberalisation also point to welfare benefit changes and reductions in social care expenditure, which have hit disabled people hard. This is true. We are living in an increasingly unsupportive society. People who previously may have received the '24/7' support which they need to lead full lives and participate in society, are now only being given basic support for their self-care needs.

This is wrong. Disabled people should not be the main victims of austerity. But I suggest that this campaign for fair welfare and independent living is not so relevant to people who are dying. Sadly, they do not have the prospect of living for many years on inadequate state support. They will qualify for what support exists, because terminally ill people are rightly given accelerated access to Personal Independence Payments and other welfare benefits. If people were making the decision to die early because of a lack of health care, hospice care or social support, then this would clearly be a terrible abuse. But the answer is to campaign for access to such support, not to block liberalisation of the law.

So in conclusion, I would certainly argue in favour of necessary safeguards in law and policy around assisted dying. I think that the law should be restricted to people who are in the final stages of terminal illness, for example, people who have six months or less to live, according to reputable medical opinion. I think people who have depression or mental illness, and are not thinking rationally, should be excluded from coverage. I think people should have to talk to two doctors and a lawyer or judge, and these professionals should be in unanimity about the suitability of the individual for the assisted dying measure. I think people should be free of pressure from relatives, carers, local authorities or service providers. I think they should have access to all relevant services, whether it is palliative care – including hospice care – independent living and other supports, or cancer drugs. In particular, I think they should have a chance to talk through options and understand how dying can be made easier by medical care. But having complied with all those criteria and considerations, I think people should be able to choose for themselves.

Assisted dying hastens an inevitable departure, and completely removes the physical distress and suffering from it. For this reason, I think it is humane and respectful of the personhood of the individual. In itself, I think this is something which Quakers will likely support. In a liberal society, law should be protective of vulnerable people, but not paternalistic. I think assisted dying legislation is consistent with disability rights values of having one's voice heard, and having choice and control over one's own life.

References

Battin M.P., van der Heide A., Ganzini L., van der Wal G. and Onwuteaka-Philipsen B.D. (2007) 'Legal physician-assisted dying in Oregon and the Netherlands: evidence concerning the impact on patients in 'vulnerable' groups', *Journal of Medical Ethics* 33: 591-597.

Eliott J.A. and Olver I.N. (2008) 'Dying cancer patients talk about euthanasia', *Social Science and Medicine* 67, 4: 647-656.

McCormack R., Clifford M. and Conroy M. (2011) 'Attitudes of UK doctors towards euthanasia and physician-assisted suicide: a systematic literature review', *Palliative Medicine* 26, 1: 23-33.

Parkinson L. et al. (2005) 'Cancer patients' attitudes towards euthanasia and physician-assisted suicide: the influence of question wording and patients' own definitions on responses', *Journal of Bioethical Inquiry* 2, 2: 82-89.

Reflections of a criminologist

Mike Nellis

As in the longstanding, if currently subdued, debate on capital punishment, public and politicians in Britain are at odds in the emerging debate on assisted dying. There is demonstrably strong public support – 82% in a 2014 survey – for the legalisation of assisted dying for mentally competent people with a terminal illness who cannot procure or effect the means to end their own lives, so long as there are safeguards to prevent its abuse. A number of sufferers, alongside their manifestly loving families, have campaigned for this, and won immense sympathy.

Although support in both the House of Lords and the House of Commons seems to be increasing – as well as in Scotland – both Parliaments have so far been unwilling to amend the Suicide Act 1961, with its maximum penalty of fourteen years for anyone who assists with the willed death of another. Nonetheless, in recognition of both the strength of popular feeling, and occasional high profile defiance of the law, guidance issued by the Director of Public Prosecution in 2010 partially decriminalised assisted dying. This was only possible where it could be shown that the deceased had competently exercised their right to die, and needed help, and where the 'assister' was demonstrably motivated by compassion for their loved one. There has been no equivalent guidance issued in Scotland, where prosecutors still prefer a jury to settle the issue.

The safeguarding issue is only a small part of the debate. Abuse is largely imagined in terms of relatives or health professionals putting

77

pressure on the dying person to end their life even more prematurely and avoid becoming a burden on, or an embarrassment to, their hard-pressed carers, or to consume precious health service resources. Lawyers are confident that procedures can be devised which would prevent and deter such behaviour – and point to examples abroad where it seems to have been accomplished - but opponents remain unpersuaded. Even the safeguard of being 'reasonably expected to die in six months', as the most recent Private Member's Bill allowed, has been contested, on the grounds that medical predictions are fallible, and patients respond idiosyncratically to treatment. No doctor can say for certain, it is said, when someone has only six months left.

Arguments against

The resistance to assisted dying for the terminally ill tends to take two not necessarily disconnected forms. On the one hand is a set of arguments, often but not always grounded in religious faith – Christian and otherwise – and a sense of life's 'sanctity', that simply sees it as morally wrong to pre-empt the allotted hour of our death, and wishes it to remain a criminal offence. In recognition that the terminally ill can suffer pain, these opponents invariably insist that palliative care can and should always be made adequate until such time as a person's life reaches its so-called natural end.

This critique tends to underplay the indignities and embarrassment of terminal illness; even if pain is well controlled, the assistance required with basic human functions, eating and toileting may be deeply distressing to a once competent and self-reliant person. The answer to this, such as it is, from people who would never countenance illness-related indignity as a ground for assisted dying, is that one's dependence on others at the end of life needs to be accepted, and that one should submit appreciatively to the ministrations of family, friends and professionals.

The second set of arguments insists that even if assisted dying for the terminally ill, taking into account both their pain and indignity, were carefully and effectively legislated for, it would set an undesirable and alarming precedent and should be avoided. It would inevitably open a Pandora's Box, it is said – or tilt us towards a slippery slope – leading either to a widening of the net of those eligible to opt for assisted dying (e.g. the mentally distressed, the world-weary) or to the coerced killing of 'invalids', or both. Slippery slope arguments are dubiously applied in politics, implying as they do that modern democracies cannot control deliberation and legislation, and choose to go so far and no further. That said, they cannot be dismissed, if only because there are voices in the new civic conversation that the western world is having about 'managing' death that have already taken law and practice beyond assisted dying for the terminally ill alone.

The spectre of eugenics undoubtedly haunts these debates, but is sometimes appealed to too readily, to cloud and discredit the ostensibly simple and narrow issue that is largely at stake in British debates on assisted dying. Nonetheless, it is not entirely irrelevant. The Nazis did kill mentally ill people and people with learning difficulties. Furthermore the elimination by the State of the unfit, the unproductive and the undesirable figures in many of the West's famous fictional dystopias, from E.M. Forster's *The Machine Stops* (the culling of the unduly athletic in a sedentary society) to William Nolan's *Logan's Run* (where in the interests of population control, no one is allowed to live beyond the age of 25), as well as in Thomas

More's more ambiguous *Utopia* itself. It is worth recalling what More imagined of life – and terminal frailty – on his peaceable and well-ordered island, not least because it focuses the vital distinction between consent and coercion in a way which people today could usefully learn from:

> The sick are carefully tended and nothing is either neglected in the way of medicine or diet which might cure them. Everything possible is done to mitigate the pain of those suffering from incurable diseases, and visitors do their best to console them by sitting and talking with them. But if the disease is not only incurable, but excruciatingly and unremittingly painful then the priests and public officials come and urge the invalid not to endure further agony. They remind him that he is now unequal to many of life's duties, a burden to himself and others; he has really outlived his own death. They tell him … he should not hesitate to free himself, or let others free him, from the rack of living. This would be a wise act, they say, since for him, death puts an end not to pleasure, but to agony. In addition, this would be obeying the advice of priests, who are interpreters of God's will; thus it will be a pious and holy act.

> Those who have been persuaded by these arguments either starve themselves to death or take a drug which frees them from life without any sensation of dying. But they never force this step on a man against his will, nor, if he decides against it, do they lessen their care of him. The man who yields to their arguments, they think, dies an honourable death; but the suicide, who takes his own life without

approval of priests and senate, him they consider unworthy of earth or fire, and they throw his body, unburied and disgraced, in the nearest bog. (Logan and Adams, 1989: 80-81.)

This explicit idealisation of choice and consent, and clear preference for what we would now call palliative care for the terminally ill by an imaginative sixteenth century writer, is impressive, but it is equally clearly set in a context in which religious and secular authorities feel justified in persuading, if not coercing, a dying person to opt for death, for the greater good. What contemporary opponents of assisted dying fear is not necessarily that 'authority' will ever become directly persuasive, still less overtly coercive, but something more insidious that would have the same consequence, namely that the decriminalisation of assisted dying would make ailing and frail people feel obliged to end their lives prematurely, for the good of others. One sees what they mean, but it is peculiar and callous to deny moral legitimacy to an ill person's own sincere desire to avoid being a burden, to imply that such feelings will arise only because others urge them upon you. Thomas More seems to have understood, several hundred years ago, the difference between legislators making a choice possible and citizens opting not to make it and, unlike him, we should not consider such an arrangement utopian. It is noteworthy that on the matter of ordinary suicide More's Catholic imagination failed him utterly: not for him, even in utopia, the Roman stoicism of a Seneca (Hadas, 1958), whose work he knew, or any empathic sense of tragic loss – just a crude desire to demean the deceased's body.

The question of autonomy

If only the debate on assisted dying for the terminally ill were simple. It is not. It cannot easily be boxed in. The debate we are having in Britain is undoubtedly parochial when compared to the ongoing debates and developments in other countries where enabling legislation for assisted dying or euthanasia has already been passed. Although the Zurich-based voluntary organisation Dignitas was only formed in 1998 (as a breakaway from an earlier organisation), medically assisted suicide has been possible in Switzerland since 1942.

Shortly after a 1997 USA Supreme Court ruling that death was not a constitutionally protected right, and that states could make their own arrangements in respect of this, Oregon legislated to allow doctors to give lethal drugs to patients with less than six months to live. The Netherlands and Belgium both legalised euthanasia in 2002, without restricting it to people with terminal illnesses. Luxembourg passed legislation in 2009. Washington state emulated Oregon's legislation in 2008. Montana and Vermont decriminalised assisted suicide in 2009 and 2013 respectively. In 2015 California became the fifth USA state to legalise assisted dying. In the same year, Canada and Columbia legislated for euthanasia.

Rachel Aviv, writing in *The New Yorker,* ruminates on the context in which these changes are taking place:

> The right-to-die movement has gained momentum at a time of anxiety about the graying of the population; people who are older than sixty-five represent the fastest growing demographic in the United States, Canada and much of

Europe. But the laws seem to be motivated less by the desires of the elderly than by the concerns of a younger generation, whose members derive comfort from the knowledge that they can control the end of their lives ... In Oregon and Switzerland, studies have shown that people who request death are less motivated by physical pain than by the desire to remain autonomous. (Aviv, 2015: 58-59)

Aviv cites the case of a 29 year-old woman with terminal brain cancer who deliberately moved to Oregon to avail herself of its services. In England, in 2015, 54 year-old Jeffrey Spector, a successful businessman, after six years of unsuccessful treatment for an inoperable spinal tumour, exercised his right to die before he became paralysed from the neck down, lost his dignity and became a burden on his family (which he expressly did not wish to be). He travelled with his wife and grown-up children to Dignitas and had a 'last supper' with relatives and other friends the night before he took poison. Opponents of assisted dying criticised Jeffrey Spector for choosing death when he could still look after himself, was in little pain, could socialise with friends and drive a car, but it could equally be argued that he chose the perfect moment, both for himself and his family, sparing them all truly unnecessary suffering. And it was surely better than a lonely suicide in England, in which his family could not have participated without risking prosecution.

In his highly compelling argument that there is indeed a Christian case for enabling assisted dying for the terminally ill, theologian Paul Badham (2009) concedes that the initially secular humanist ideal of individual personal autonomy has, at an intellectual level at least, created difficulties for many Christians, schooled as they once were in a deep sense of God's providential ordering of the world, up to and including each person's last breath, coupled with a divine demand for subservience to his will. But as the nineteenth and the twentieth centuries progressed, the ordinary everyday lives of most western Christians became as infused with the possibility of choices on work, education and healthcare as any other citizen, enabled by complex cultural, political and technological transformations.

Badham is by no means alone, theologically speaking, in believing that personal autonomy can be appropriated as a Christian ideal, or even in his confidence that on the strength of it Christians could endorse assisted dying for those terminally ill people who want it. Nonetheless, he underplays how far-reaching the consequences of a secular conviction that one's life is one's own to dispose of (figuratively or literally) could become to growing swathes of people – those who live precarious lives in increasingly unequal and insecure, devil-take-the-hindmost societies, whose governments abjure or reduce responsibility for their citizens' wellbeing. He does not consider the possibility of deep and enduring personal unhappiness, grounded in a physical or mental condition that falls short of terminal, perhaps exacerbated by poverty, becoming a reason for wanting the right to die. That is, in fact, an all too plausible consequence of feeling isolated, self-contained and responsible for one's own fate – the ingredients of autonomy – in a world which may seem to some, already, to offer diminishing means and reasons for continuing to live.

The world-weary old man who checks into a government euthanasia centre in a near-future, welfare-free New York, in the 1973 movie *Soylent Green*, may be more of a harbinger than he seemed at the time. Ever diminishing investment in public mental health services

– even more so than palliative care for the old and sick – may be more of a factor in future right to die debates than we anticipate, if not necessarily in Britain, then certainly elsewhere. Recent government advice on managing suicide, issued to frontline staff in Job Centres as they are pushed into paring down the life chances of claimants to ever less bearable levels, may not seem at present to be connected to right to die debates, culturally or politically (Nutt, 2015). But perhaps one day we will look back and see that ugly moment differently.

Developments in Belgium

Certainly events and controversies in Belgium give food for thought. Belgium's 2002 euthanasia legislation – a radically humanist repudiation of a burdensome Catholic cultural heritage – was never restricted only to people with terminal illnesses. It took account from the start of unbearable psychological suffering for which there was no prospect of a cure. Two medical practitioners are required to authorise euthanasia in the cases of terminal illness, three when psychological suffering is involved. Doctors administer lethal drugs themselves. Fourteen hundred people in Belgium were granted euthanasia in 2012, eighteen hundred in 2013: numbers have increased 150% in five years. Most of them had cancer, but people with autism, anorexia, borderline personality disorder, chronic-fatigue syndrome, partial paralysis, blindness coupled with deafness, and manic depression, dementia and dissatisfaction with failed sex change surgery have also exercised their right to die (Aviv, 2015). Debates have taken place about the age at which children might wish to exercise a right to die.

Cases involving psychiatric patients were uncommon in the years immediately after 2002, but complaints that their mental suffering were being taken less seriously than the suffering of physically ill people led gradually to more applications being granted. Euthanasia seems generally accepted in Belgium, supported by the majority of, if not all, doctors and academics and the population at large. The country has the second highest suicide rate in Europe, and some doctors believe that the availability of euthanasia as a medical service encourages people who would not otherwise do so to come forward to discuss their feelings of hopelessness – some of whom, after counselling, opt to live. Euthanasia is openly explored in secular, humanistic ethics classes in schools. Medical Professor Wim Distelmans, of the Free University in Brussels, one of the authors of the 2002 legislation, who has euthanised over a hundred people himself, is something of a celebrity commentator on the matter in Belgium.

Two cases

Aviv (2015) writes at length about the case of Godelieva de Troyer, a 63 year-old, middle class woman with grown-up children and grandchildren with a long history of depression (considered incurable by her psychiatrist). In 2011 she asked Distelmans to expedite her death. He did so on April 19th 2012. Although Godelieva had notified her son Tom, whom she saw infrequently, of her intention to undergo euthanasia, she deliberately did not indicate when it would take place, and Tom was only told the day afterwards. This distressed him, and he embarked on a public campaign to challenge Distelmans' right to take his mother's wish to die at face value, without insisting on a reunion with her son and grandchildren. He had in fact suggested this, but Godelieva had rejected it. Her son had hoped that it might have assuaged her loneliness and given her second thoughts. At every turn of his campaign to assert relatives' rights in decisions of this kind, Tom was told that correct procedures had been followed, and that it was his mother's free will to die – her right to self-determination – without seeking a reunion with him or taking account of his views. Tom's standpoint is a minority view, but it is not unique: other relatives have filed criminal complaints against the doctors involved. As Aviv (2015: 63) notes, however, the investigative process is confidential and, in the past thirteen years, no case has been referred for prosecution.

Even more interesting, from a criminological perspective, is the case of Frank Van den Bleeken (Willems, 2015). In September 2014 a Belgian appeal court granted an application for euthanasia to this man, a prisoner who was into his thirtieth year of custody with no prospect of release, and claimed to be 'suffering unbearably' from the incurable mental illness which was responsible for his incarceration. He had never been convicted of the murder and rape with which he had been charged: he had been deemed insane and detained indefinitely on psychiatric grounds, in the expectation that he would receive treatment for his condition. No such treatment was actually available in Belgium, and after a spell in psychiatric detention he was placed in an ordinary prison. Van den Bleeken accepts both his illness and that he is a danger to society, and is not seeking release from confinement. Death, however, was not his first option. He applied first for a transfer to a treatment facility in the Netherlands, and only when that was refused, in 2011, did he apply for euthanasia. The justice department opposed this in court, but eventually lost on appeal. Fifteen other detainees are thought to have applied for euthanasia. Van den Bleeken, however, was not granted his wish to die, although the reason why has not been disclosed on the grounds of medical confidentiality.

The case stimulated debate about Belgium's penal system and its euthanasia laws more generally. Two sisters of one of his victims complained that euthanasia would enable him to evade deserved punishment, but as he had never actually been convicted this argument could not be sustained. The appeal court granted his application not in order to enable merciful release from a long period of detention but rather because his mental illness was accepted as incurable. Nonetheless, one psychiatrist has publicly doubted whether it is actually possible to disentangle Van den Bleeken's mental condition from the conditions of his detention; the fact of long-term imprisonment cannot but make mental illness less bearable.

This very intelligible concern has played into the broader debate about Belgium's persistent failure to provide adequate psychiatric treatment in its prison system. The European Court of Human Rights had already found against Belgium in this respect, in 2013, construing failure to offer appropriate treatment to a mentally ill sex offender as 'inhuman and degrading'. The problem is systemic, not merely a question of individual cases. Ordinary prisons do not have the facilities at all. Transfers to specialised facilities are limited by the number of places in them, and procedures for transfer abroad, possible in principle, are complex. New penal-psychiatric facilities are being built in Belgium, but the pace of improvement is slow and it is not a political priority. In their absence, it is unlikely that any Belgian prisoners will actually be subject to euthanasia, even while the law still allows them to apply for it.

Conclusion

It is not difficult to see why Quakers might support the narrow and specific compassionate demand for the legalisation of assisted dying of the terminally ill, and it ought, in theory, to be possible to do this. It would be desirable to do so. But it is not only dystopian fears of a slippery slope that make this less simple and less easy than it appears. There are already examples in the nearby world of assisted dying legislation which goes into territory that Quakers – and even secular humanists – are likely to find less comfortable, however logical and plausible they may seem, on analysis, to be.

Longstanding Quaker traditions of commitment to social reform and the constant improvement of human wellbeing probably preclude any easy acceptance of a right to die being granted to people because welfare and psychiatric services are not available to them, or because they were dissatisfied with what was available, and find death more attractive than life. 'Friendship' in its deepest sense requires that we build convivial institutions in which this is never so, and uphold the forms of knowledge and expertise that enable us to understand and assuage the most acute human despair. Quaker psychiatrist Bob Johnson's fierce conviction that no mental disorder is incurable (Johnson, 2010) seems relevant to Frank Van den Bleeken's case, and the question of how lifelong detention for dangerous people can be made spiritually and emotionally bearable – if indeed it can – must be addressed in any country that allows natural life sentences, as Britain now does.

Perhaps Quakers could help by challenging the intemperate language in which the debate on assisted dying is often conducted, and usher in a more respectful vocabulary. Each side has a tendency to portray the other as heartless or sinister, as if each had a hidden agenda, and this makes clear argument difficult. In Scotland, for example, opponents of assisted dying claimed that its supporters were promoting a 'duty to be dead', and a notionally impartial government committee warned against 'communicating an offensive message to certain members of the community (many of whom may be particularly vulnerable) that society would regard it as "reasonable" rather than tragic if they wished to end their lives' (quoted in Puttick, 2015). This presented a travesty of the views of assisted dying's supporters.

Paul Badham's book is a model of lucid analysis and sensitive language and Quakers could well start from there – whether they accept his belief in an afterlife or not, because his core argument does not finally depend on it (although in his terms, it strengthens it). Badham is right that there should be a legislative framework in which compassion can be shown to the terminally ill who wish to end their lives with their loved ones around them, but creating that space will be easier said than done, because the right to die debate has already moved beyond the particular needs and wishes of the terminally ill, and in future we will need the intellectual competence to address all the issues that that raises, particularly what it says about the *mores* of contemporary society.

References

Aviv, R. (2015) 'The Death Treatment: when should people with a non-terminal illness be allowed to die?' *The New Yorker*, 22nd June 2015: 56-65.

Badham, P. (2009) *Is there a Christian Case for Assisted Dying?* London: SPCK.

Hadas, M (1958) 'On Suicide' in *The Stoic Philosophy of Seneca: Essays and Letters,* New York: W. W. Norton and Company.

Johnson, B. (2010) 'The Trauma Challenge: a neo-medical model of psychiatry' on Dr Bob Johnson's website: www.truthtrustconsent.com

Logan, G. M. and Adams, R. M. (eds) (1989) *Thomas More's Utopia*, Cambridge: Cambridge University Press.

Nutt, K. (2015) 'Reforms leave benefit claimants with 'nothing to live for', say MSPs after suicide guidance issued to DWP staff,' *The National,* 24th August 2015.

Puttick, H. (2015) 'Conscience vote for MSP's on Suicide Bill', *The Herald,* 1stMay 2015.

Willems, A. (2015) 'Euthanasia of a detainee: granting a prisoner's request', *Criminal Justice Matters*, issue 1999, March 2015: 16-17.

Autonomy and dignity:
A Quaker theological response to assisted dying

Benjamin J. Wood

It is perhaps useful to begin by sketching out what this essay is not. It is not principally an attempt to explore the legal or medical complexities of assisted dying. It does not advocate a particular model of care for those suffering from terminal illnesses. It is not a straightforward apology for or against those who advocate a change in the law to permit physician-assisted suicide. What it attempts to do instead is a deeper yet more limited task. It considers what a Quaker theological response to assisted dying might look like – acknowledging, at the same time, the pitfalls of undertaking such an enterprise. 'Theological' here is meant in the rich Quaker sense of speech and action arising from our experience of God.

Of course, any Quaker publication professing to be doing moral theology is always liable to provoke mixed reactions, and rightly so. It is a hazardous business rooting any ethical discussion in any idea of God (prone as that is to all kinds of distortions and accretions). Yet, its dangers aside, this is what Quakers have always done. Our testimonies are imperfect and muddled expressions of how a communal encounter with God changed us, and continues to do so. Our corporate moral convictions as Quakers are not picked from a pleasant conveyor belt of 'causes' but emerge from centuries of standing before the Mystery (God, Spirit, the Other Reality) and seeking to name it and follow it truthfully, without guile or evasion. What have such encounters taught us both about the meaning of life and death? To consider this question we must first ascertain what the differences are between Quaker and secular ways of approaching moral decision-making.

The solitary walker as secular morality

1778 was a grim year for Jean-Jacques Rousseau. The once fashionable philosopher was caught up in a bout of melancholy which, try as he might, he could not shake off. Now in old age Rousseau surveyed his life and found much to mourn over. His books were being neglected by an irritable public while his philosophy was widely derided in the fashionable salons of France. As Rousseau tells us in his last book, *Reveries of the Solitary Walker*:

> I am alone in the world, with no brother, neighbour or friend, or any company left me but my own. The most sociable and loving of men has with one accord been cast out by all the rest. With all the ingenuity of hate they have sought out the cruelest torture of my sensitive soul, and have violently broken all the threads that bound me to them... So now they are strangers and foreigners; they no longer exist for me, since such is their will. But I, detached as I am from them and from the whole world, what am I? (Rousseau, 1979: 27)

This is an old theme for Rousseau. In an earlier work, *Discourse on Inequality*, Rousseau had mapped a new myth of human prehistory, which was in tune with the emancipatory ambitions of the European Enlightenment. Once, human beings had been self-sufficient and solitary creatures who exhibited neither violence nor avarice. Exile from this state of innocence comes for Rousseau in the garb of civilisation. By living in ever more circumscribed groups, human

94

beings give up their extensive private freedoms to act and replace these with security and co-operation. Yet there is a cost. In the new order our deepest longings are silenced, replaced by 'irksome duty and obligation' (Rousseau, 1979: 48) which distorts and curtails our original desires. As Rousseau sighs:

> If I had remained free, unknown and isolated as nature meant me to be, I should have done nothing but good, for my heart does not contain the seeds of any harmful passion. (Rousseau, 1979: 101)

Since its initial telling, Rousseau's narrative of melancholic individualism has continued to be retold in manifold ways. In part, the story appeals because it offers a philosophical alternative to the rather bleak view that people are merely extensions of their community or culture. Rousseau wants to get to the 'inner man' where neither society nor community can intrude. Yet, if Rousseau's story has a liberating power, it also has the potential to reduce our sense of what it means to be human. By stressing the self-directing facilities in human beings, Rousseau's way of looking at the world is liable to commit two excesses. In the first place, by emphasising the value of isolation, freedom to choose becomes disconnected from any sense of community. People are set adrift to make their own destiny, in a world which is inherently hostile to them. True, such drift bestows responsibility, but it also makes every failure or weakness a personal fault. Autonomy in this extreme form may manifest as an acute sense of self-hatred, as we continually confront the fact that we are frequently unable to bring our desires to fruition.

In the second place (and this should concern us particularly as Friends) an over-emphasis upon autonomy can diminish the ultimate significance of human life. By stressing the primacy of personal choice, there can be no room for a higher direction or shape to our existence, since the demand of another (whether God or the community) may place our freedom in peril. The most immediate effect of this stance is its corrosive effect upon the substance of moral beliefs. We may speak of justice and peace but, in the cosmos as described by Rousseau, these can be no more than pleasant fictions to obscure and flatter the private desires of these autonomous individuals as they await death. In this roving spirit, assisted dying is as unproblematic as any other personal decision. The vital thing is not the shape of the choice but whether it was undertaken freely and is an approximate expression of our desires. Yet, what if one concedes that there is more to life than willing and desiring? What if life has a shape and meaning beyond our preferences?

These radical possibilities lie at the very heart of Quaker life and worship. In the silence of Meeting we are invited into an order not our own. In prayerful waiting, we attempt to heed a Life and Power which is communicated through us. When Friends say they feel unexpectedly 'loved' in meeting, they point to a deep structure of the world, a reality that acts in us, regardless of our cynicism or emotional coldness towards its activity. What might this, the Other Reality, demand of Friends when we ponder assisted dying? How might the love that greets us in worship inform our practice towards those in states of agony and despair? In the next section, I consider what resources Quaker theology may have for articulating an answer.

Being human and the Quaker way

At the heart of the Quaker vision of ethics is the promise of personal and corporate transformation by a reality outside us. As George Fox described this transformation in his *Journal*:

> Now I was come up in spirit through the flaming sword, into the paradise of God. All things were new; and all the creation gave unto me another smell than before, beyond what words can utter. I knew nothing but pureness, and innocency, and righteousness; *being renewed into the image of God by Christ Jesus, to the state of Adam, which he was in before he fell* (BW italics). The creation was opened to me; and it was showed me how all things had their names given them according to their nature and virtue. (Fox, 1998: 32)

Notice the phrase 'into the image of God'. For Fox, being Quaker means having one's deepest nature renewed so that one's life (including one's moral choices) becomes a mirror and conduit for divine love and creativity. This new direction to life was sometimes 'Gospel Order', a phrase which attempted to encapsulate the sense that the Good News of God was being revealed and unfolded throughout the whole of reality. As the American Friend Lloyd Lee Wilson points out:

> Gospel Order is the order established by God that exists in every part of creation, transcending the chaos that seems so often prevalent. It is right relationship of every part of creation, however small, to every other part and to the Creator. (Wilson, 1993: 3)

What are the immediate implications of this account of human beings?

In the secular West, many treat moral deliberation as a deductive enterprise concerned with 'buying off' various interests or simply muddling through without violence. In contrast to this rather threadbare conception of ethics, for first-generation Friends moral campaigns were the means of bringing the world into closer conformity with the intent of God. Understood in morally personalist terms, Friends attempted to speak to the submerged image of God (the source of peace and justice) in all they met, awakening hearts and minds to the 'light which enlightens everyone who comes into the world' (John 1:1). Since the initial formation of the Quaker movement in the 1640s, Quaker thinkers have added much to this conception of divine image, extending its ethical implications with each passing century. In our own time, concerns over the well-being of the natural world have prompted some Friends to apply the language of divine image to ecosystems and the lives of non-human animals (see Adams, 1996: 72). The richness of an ethics of divine image has also been further extended by the increasing recourse of Friends to a negative (or apophatic) way of speaking about God. As Harvey Gillman expresses this latter-day turn in Quaker thinking:

> A recognition of the will of God as part of the very fabric of the world around us; a sense of awe at the magnitude of existence, an outpouring of the self to the other; these all lead to a struggle with the inadequacy of language. When words fall away there is stillness and silence, and then there is that which is beyond word and silence. Perhaps even the word God falls away. (Gillman, 2007: 119)

What does this apophatic turn mean for Quaker talk of the divine image? If no words can properly comprehend the mystery of God, then to speak of the 'image of God' involves honouring the participation of a given life in the Mystery of Being. What some call 'the sanctity of life' is in fact the refusal of a life to ever conform to a single interpretation or category. There are always hidden possibilities and depths that we often cannot comprehend. We might say that to be a person means being understood and constituted as a question made flesh – the answer to which comes from God (that source of all mystery and depth). To support the dignity of this living question mark requires respecting and affirming these unforeseen potentialities. Conversely, the moment we attempt to reduce a person to a single facet (their bodily capacities, their intelligence, or their usefulness in relation to some wider social purpose) we dishonour the mystery of the person. This is the kernel of what we Quakers mean when we affirm 'the worth of every individual as a child of God'. (*Quaker faith & practice [Qf&p]*, 2013: 23.31)

The mystery of personhood

What then is ruled in and ruled out by this theological vision of the person? In the first place, a Quaker understanding of ethics will not allow us to simply translate the language of an autonomous death into our own theological grammar, without at least some hesitation. After all, as Friends we believe that life has a shape which transcends our immediate wants and expectations. Our lives are not wholly our own, but reflect a pattern larger than ourselves. At the very least, Friends should be highly sceptical of any attempt to repackage assisted dying as part of an 'end-of-life choice'. Such language suggests that assisted suicide is merely another neutral option among others, not the choice which ends further choice. This is doubly so in the case of a person who feels that the only freedom they can exercise is to be found in their death. Such a choice suggests a negation of the mystery of selfhood. Now the sufferer feels herself totally identified with her suffering; she feels herself becoming wholly her illness. In such a situation, the only way out is to embrace death, so that (paradoxically) a remnant of a living mystery might be retained. This is a tragedy, because it forces an image of God from the world.

It is also a tragic process for those who carry out the destruction of a life. When our tradition speaks of the 'divine image' it frequently does so in connection with a larger life: the emergence of radical possibilities, a new state of being bursting into existence (see Muers, 2015: 73). This is vividly expressed in the older Quaker use of the word 'Seed' for the Inward Light. For a manifestation of the 'image' to be the instrument of the death of another image-bearer suggests a distortion of the life-giving nature of the mystery which is at the heart of being itself. Such a conclusion has prescience, since it is consistent with other ethical commitments found among Friends. As Britain Yearly Meeting noted in 1956 on the abolition of the death penalty:

> The sanctity of human life is one of the fundamentals of a Christian society and can in no circumstances be set aside... The sanctioning by the State of the taking of human life has a debasing effect on the community, and tends to produce the very brutality which it seeks to prevent. (*Qf&p*, 2013: 23.97)

A Quaker ethic which favoured assisted dying in cases of terminal illness would have to show that a general commitment to autonomy would not erode our unconditional commitment to the dignity of other persons in differing circumstances. I do not believe that such reassurance has yet been produced. Those who support the rightness of assisted dying in principle are, I think, rightly going to contest my suggestion that there is any tension at all between such honouring and allowing a person to kill themselves (especially if we honour death as part of the sacredness of life). Then the question becomes, how do we ensure that the death of a person sufficiently honours that person's life? But what does such reverence even mean if its object is to bring a person's life to an end?

One possible road for supporters would be to consider the Quaker attitude towards torture as morally analogous to the experience of the terminally ill. Friends continue to oppose torture on the grounds that 'We believe in the worth of every individual as a child of God, and that no circumstances whatsoever can justify practices intended to break bodies, minds and spirits' (*Qf&p*, 2013:23.31). Is the refusal of assisted suicide to a terminally ill patient a similar violation of a person's 'divine image'? Some are persuaded of this line of reasoning, yet such a formulation is fraught with difficulties. A terminally ill person may be in intense pain, but can this be said to be torture? Does a well-trained and compassionate palliative care worker really engage in the degrading treatment of other human beings? Moreover, can the Quaker rejection of torture be said to apply to situations where the goal of medical practice is to sustain life? Such ambiguities of meaning are highly suggestive of the need for more discernment in the years ahead concerning not only Quaker attitudes to the person, but our corporate perspective on the meaning of suffering.

A Quaker palliative vision

Where does this all lead us? In its rejection of a wholly autonomous and isolated model of the individual, Quaker ethics asks some tough questions regarding any form of physician-assisted suicide. First of all we must learn to be critical about the justifications we are offered for assisted dying and look for the stories and assumptions which may lie behind them. In confronting the tragic nature of assisted death, we should ask ourselves what role we as a society have played in making death an 'option' for so many people. Is it merely the intensity of pain and infirmity which drives contemporary discussions, or something deeper? Has a severely ill person come to the conclusion that her life is not worth living because he or she has failed to gain independence from others? Is the wish to die in some cases a response to our society's obsession with the dream of perpetual autonomy?

In the light of these probing questions, we Quakers need to be resolute in offering an alternative story about the meaning of being human. A rich source for such an alternative vision is to listen attentively to Friends with disabilities. Many with impairments learn early on that life must be understood through a prism other than absolute freedom. The experience of being wounded or frail can teach us much about the universal experience of being human. In reality we all need help in the course of our lives and, by necessity, are sustained by the generosity and gifts of others. But in a culture which glorifies personal achievement, it is hard to let go of the fiction that we are self-created beings. For those· who develop infirmities and limitations over time, it is acutely painful to let go of once unquestioned depictions of ourselves. For those in the later stages of terminal illness, a sense of dependence upon others to

102

whom we are close may feel crushing. Yet, such dependence will only crush if we buy into the myth of the solitary walker. Suffering and needfulness is not a personal failure; it is a mark of a shared condition.

Unlike Rousseau, we do not understand ourselves as isolated individuals expected to lift ourselves up when we fall. We are called to live with and for others in society. This is not a restriction, a personal weakness or a primordial fall, but part of what it means to be fully human. Underlying this ethic of interdependence is our spiritual experience as Friends. While those with severely debilitating illnesses may be viewed as burdens to a society which wants nothing to stand in the way of instant satisfaction, the love we experience in our worship together leaves no-one behind. In our diminishing capacities, we know that the Spirit meets us and affirms us in the things which are eternal – never forgetting us, never forsaking us. In accord with this divine affirmation, we are challenged to affirm in turn: upholding those who suffer while refusing to forget the deep and abiding mystery of their humanity.

Does our faithfulness to the divine image mean that the living mystery of the person must be preserved at all costs, even at the price of needless suffering? It does not seem a violation of the dignity of the person to withdraw medical treatment which is keeping a patient alive. The same can be said of the use of pain-relieving drugs which also have the side-effect of shortening life. Such undertakings do not constitute an active choice to destroy life, but may hasten its end. This is not hypocrisy but an attempt to preserve the dignity of the person, while acknowledging the complexities and trade-offs of attending compassionately to a person suffering from terminal illness. Insofar as such a trail of thought amounts to a Quaker vision for the terminally ill, it is deeply palliative. The primary ethical concern in such a situation should be the comfort of the person, so that to the greatest extent possible their dignity is preserved. For some, even in the midst of intense suffering, a measure of tranquility might be found. Such moments of spiritual refreshment (time for prayer or worshipful silence) while not abating all their anguish, may offer solace and peace in ways that medical treatment alone cannot provide.

I feel sure that not all Friends will be convinced by this palliative interpretation of Quaker ethics in this area. Indeed, some will suggest that the sanctity of life as I have sketched it here is merely a poetic device, or inhumane torture of the terminally ill in the name of an abstract principle. Yet such a principle is not abstract for Quakers and never has been. The notion that life is precious and needs protecting is woven into our experience of worship and the words we use before God. Given such a conclusion, how should those with significant unease regarding assisted dying respond to those who may wish for that option when the time comes? Faithfulness to the divine image also means loving those Friends who (even with the best palliative medicine) decide that they must be helped to take their own lives. We must seek to understand the choices people have taken, even if we are concerned and unsettled by those choices. Our plea as disquieted Friends should be simply this: whatever you feel is right, lay it before God and your Meeting, and test your discernment. There has been a tendency among Friends to view the rightness and wrongness of assisted dying as a purely personal matter. However, such a position merely reinforces the sense that there is no higher pattern to the world other than the one we devise. But this is not really going with the grain of the Quaker Way.

When we make claims about the meaning of life and death, do we do so as individuals (with our Quakerism as an add-on) or do we navigate these matters as Quakers? Do we use the methods of Quaker clearness to test our concern? Or are we content with our knowledge and experience? Are we prepared to be led, and to abide by, what is discerned in the course of worshipful discernment? These matters are pressing for those who find themselves concerned about assisted dying. Yet, if Quaker ethics challenges us to live more interdependent lives, it also offers us a key consolation. In a profound sense, contemporary ways of thinking lure us into assuming that on the deepest level we all live and die alone, but Quakers have never believed this. Our lives and our deaths are joined to a power of love and life which gives all our individual stories meaning, regardless of frailty, infirmity or illness.

References

Adams, A. (ed.) (1996) *The Creation was Open to Me: An Anthology of Friends' Writings on that of God in all Creation*, Wilmslow: Quaker Green Concern.

Fox, G. (1998) *The Journal*, Harmondsworth: Penguin.

Gillman, H. (2007) *Consider the Blackbird: Reflections on Spirituality and Language*, London: Quaker Books.

Muers, R. (2015) *Testimony: Quakerism and Theological Ethics*, London: SCM.

Quaker faith & practice (2013): The Book of Christian Discipline of the Yearly Meeting of the Religious Society of Friends (Quakers) in Britain, 5th edn, London: Religious Society of Friends (Quakers) in Britain.

Rousseau, J-J. (1979) *Reveries of the Solitary Walker*, trans. Peter France, London: Penguin Classics.

Wilson, L.L. (1993) *Essays on the Quaker Vision of Gospel Order*, Pennsylvania: Quaker Press.

The morality of assisting others to die

Jeff McMahan

My concern in this short article is with the morality of assisting people to die. My arguments are secular in character but are compatible with the assumptions of many theists.

There are various ways in which one person may assist another to die. Although the word 'assist' seems to imply that the assister acts in accordance with the will of the person assisted, the issue of assistance in dying can extend beyond those cases in which a person autonomously requests assistance in dying. There are, for example, instances in which it may seem that it would be better for an individual to die but in which the individual cannot request or consent to being helped to die – for example, cases involving infants or individuals with profound dementia. Toward the end I will offer a few remarks about problems that can arise when an individual with dementia has left an Advance Decision indicating a desire to die should he become sufficiently demented to be unable to think rationally about whether to continue to live. Otherwise I will be concerned only with cases in which a person has an expressed and autonomously formed desire for assistance in dying at the time that the assistance might be given.

Although most of the ways of assisting a person to die are active, some are essentially passive. Perhaps the least controversial instance of assisting another person to die is the withdrawal of life support from a person who wishes to die. Suppose, for example, that a physician has placed a person on a life-support machine but that the person now wishes to die and therefore wants the machine removed, but cannot easily remove it himself – or, perhaps, cannot remove it at all by himself, perhaps because he is paralysed. The assistance the person requests from the physician is therefore only the removal of the life-support machine that she has provided.

Suppose that the physician provides that assistance and the person dies. No one, it seems, has engaged in an act of killing. The person to whom the life-support machine was connected has allowed himself to die from the condition from which the machine had been saving him. In requesting that the machine be removed, he has done no more than he would have done in refusing to allow it to be connected to him in the first place. Yet, even though he has not killed himself, his action counts as suicide because his intention in allowing himself to die from the condition was to end his life. Moreover, just as he does not kill himself, so the physician who removed the life-support machine did not kill him either. By removing the machine that she had provided as a means of saving the person, she merely stopped saving him. By stopping saving him, she allowed him to die – or, more precisely, allowed him to allow himself to die.

These are, of course, merely descriptions of what has been done. But they may help to explain why it is hard to believe that either the person or the physician has acted impermissibly – assuming that the person's death was better for him than continuing to live and was not seriously harmful to anyone else. For one of the concerns about assisting a person to die is that doing so involves killing and killing is usually wrong. Yet assisting someone to die need not and usually does not involve killing him, even when the person assisted then kills himself.

If, for example, a physician provides a person with a lethal drug that the person then administers to himself, the physician does not kill the person but merely facilitates the person's killing himself. And in a case of this sort, the act of assistance derives its moral status primarily from the moral status of the assisted act. If the person's act of killing himself is permissible, there is a presumption that the physician's act of providing the means of his doing so should be permissible as well. There may be some exceptions when other considerations bear on the case – for example, if the physician is a beneficiary of the person's will and provides the lethal drug with the sole intention of gaining an inheritance sooner rather than later. Philosophers disagree about cases of this sort, with some arguing that the bad intention makes the act impermissible and others arguing that the intention is irrelevant to the morality of the act. Or it may be that in certain circumstances, an act is permissible only for a certain person or persons but not for anyone else. For example, it may be permissible for a parent to kill an innocent bystander as a side effect of saving her child but not permissible for a disinterested third party to do so. Again, philosophers disagree. But such exceptions, if there are any, are rare and in general it seems that assisting a person to do an act that it is permissible for that person to do must itself be permissible, particularly if the assister acts with the same intention as the person assisted.

Suicide

If this is right, it shifts the question from the permissibility of assisting someone to die to the permissibility of a person's intentionally bringing about her own death – that is, to the permissibility of suicide. This is an issue on which common beliefs have changed radically. It used to be widely believed that suicide is

109

a serious form of wrongdoing – a grave sin, as it would have been expressed by most of those who held this belief. It was thought that suicide, at least in its active form, is an instance of murder, as it involves the intentional killing of an innocent person (innocent, at least, until the act of self-killing is done). It made no moral difference, on that view, that the person murdered and the murderer were the same person or that the murder was done with the consent of the person murdered. But beliefs about the morality of suicide have changed almost as much as beliefs about the morality of slavery over the past few centuries. Most of us believe it profoundly mistaken, and even morally wrong, because inhumane, to suppose that someone driven by misfortune to kill herself is a murderer who is guilty of grave wrongdoing.

Even in the past when beliefs about suicide were so different, those who condemned suicide struggled to reconcile their harsh view of typical suicides with their admiration for those who intentionally sacrificed their lives for the sake of others. Consider the well-known example of the soldier who, instead of leaping to safety, throws himself on a grenade to save the lives of his fellow soldiers. I doubt that anyone has ever argued that such a person is guilty of self-murder. The obvious reply is that this person does not commit suicide because he does not intend to end his own life, but only to save the lives of others. And indeed I think it is right to say that because this person does not intend his own death, he does not commit suicide. But that is a point about language, not morality. It is also true of such a person that he does what he knows will kill him and that he does this as an intended means of achieving an aim. And when a person kills *another person* in this way, we consider it murder. Suppose that instead of throwing himself on the grenade, the soldier grabs one of his fellow soldiers and throws him on the grenade. In this case too he does not intend that his fellow soldier die. This is shown by the fact that nothing he wants to achieve would be thwarted if the grenade failed to explode or if the other soldier were merely maimed rather than killed. What he does intend is to use the other soldier's body as means of shielding himself from the explosion if the grenade explodes, and that is sufficient to make him a murderer if the grenade does explode and the other soldier is killed.

What this shows is that intentionally killing oneself, or doing what one knows will kill oneself, is morally quite different from intentionally killing another, or doing what one knows will kill another, without that other person's consent. In most or all instances in which we are not permitted to sacrifice another as a means of achieving some end, we are permitted to sacrifice ourselves. And just as it can be permissible to kill oneself as a means of benefiting others, so it can be permissible to kill oneself as a means of benefiting oneself (by preventing oneself from having to endure a future that would be on balance intrinsically bad), provided that one's doing so is not seriously harmful to others.

There are circumstances in which it can be morally wrong for a person to kill himself even when death would be better for him than continuing to live. What could make it wrong to kill oneself when it would be better for oneself to die is that it would be seriously harmful to others. For example, a person who has small children who depend on him and would be damaged for life if he were to kill himself might be morally required to continue to endure an intrinsically bad existence for the sake of his children.

But when it really is better for a person's own sake that he die rather than continue to live, his dying would seldom be more harmful to others than his continuing to live would be. Perhaps the most common reason why one person's death is harmful to others is that the others love him, so that his death would leave a void in their lives. But when a person's continuing to live would be intrinsically bad for him – for example, because his suffering would outweigh any good experiences he might have – it is hard to imagine that it could be genuinely better for those who love him that he should continue to suffer rather than bring his suffering to an end. Those who love him should find it easier to reconcile themselves to what is better for him rather than to what is worse for him.

Some philosophers, influenced by the views of the German philosopher Immanuel Kant, argue that human beings have or contain an intrinsic value or worth (often referred to as 'human dignity') that is independent of whether their lives go well or badly and that is inviolable for the sake of any other value, including their own well-being. Some of these philosophers infer from this that intentionally to bring about one's own death, whether by doing or allowing, is always or nearly always wrong because it involves the sacrifice of an incomparably greater value for the sake of a lesser value. As Kant himself expressed it in his *Metaphysics of Morals*, 'disposing of oneself as a mere means to some discretionary end is debasing in one's person (homo noumenon), to which man (homo phenomenon) was nevertheless entrusted for preservation.' A person's avoidance of suffering is, according to Kant and his contemporary followers, a discretionary end.

There are, however, many respects in which this view is objectionable. If it is we ourselves who have a kind of value that demands respect, it seems that keeping ourselves in existence when continued existence is intrinsically bad for us is not a way of respecting our own value but is incompatible with such respect. This may explain why many Kantians write as if it is not we ourselves who have this inviolable value but is instead something we *possess* – namely, human dignity, which is 'entrusted to [us] for preservation'. But then it seems that the Kantian view requires us to see *ourselves* as mere means to the preservation of a dignity of which we are mere custodians. I know of nothing plausible that could be said in defence of such a view. Most Kantians identify our 'rational nature' as that which is the basis of our human dignity. Their objection to suicide is that it involves sacrificing one's rational nature as a means of gaining relief from suffering. But this seems to imply, implausibly, that using stupefying analgesics, such as morphine, to gain relief from suffering is also impermissible.

It seems to me, therefore, that we should accept that it can be morally permissible for a person to kill herself or allow herself to die because death would be better for her than continued life, provided that her dying would not be seriously harmful to others, particularly those who are specially related to her, such as her children. And if that is right, it seems that in most cases it is permissible for a third party to assist such a person to die. This is because in most cases it is permissible for a third party to help enable a person to do what it is permissible for that person to do.

This, however, states the case far too weakly. It is not merely that it can be permissible to help a person to die when that person's life will no longer be worth living. It can be our duty to do so. When, as is the case in most societies now, assisting another person to die is illegal, those who rationally seek to die but are unwilling to expose their loved ones or others to a risk of legal penalties are forced to end their lives by themselves. This may mean that they are compelled to die alone, in despair or terror, without comfort from those whom they love and who love them. It also means that they risk failing in the attempt to die, leaving themselves not only alive but also humiliated and possibly disabled or disfigured. As the author, Arthur Koestler, once observed, 'there is only one prospect worse than being chained to an intolerable existence: the nightmare of a botched attempt to end it.'

As I mentioned earlier, there are various ways of assisting another person to die. Thus far I have discussed only assisting someone to act in a way by which she brings about her own death, either by killing herself or by allowing herself to die. But assisting someone to die may also require killing that person. This may be the case when the person is incapable of either killing herself or allowing herself to die (as in the case of someone who is tethered to life-support machines but is paralysed and cannot disconnect herself from them). As I indicated earlier, many people think that there is a special moral objection to killing another person that does not apply either to killing oneself or to assisting another person to kill herself. I will argue, however, that in the cases with which we are concerned – namely, those in which death would be better for a person and not seriously harmful to others, and in which the person autonomously requests to be killed – it is a mistake to think that killing would be wrong even though it could be permissible for the person to kill herself or permissible for a third party to assist her to bring about her own death.

Most people believe that in general it is more seriously morally objectionable to kill an innocent person than it is to allow an innocent person to die. Most of us could, in the near future, prevent some innocent person from dying – for example, by donating bone marrow, or a kidney, or by simply giving a sufficient amount of money to a charity organisation engaged in saving lives in some impoverished area of the world. Yet most of us do not do this. And even when we become aware that we have allowed people to die when we could have saved them, we do not feel that we have acted as wrongly as someone who has killed an innocent person. Indeed, most people feel that they have not acted wrongly at all. We therefore conclude that killing a person is morally worse than letting a person die, and we extend this belief to our thinking about euthanasia.

Euthanasia

But the idea that there is a moral asymmetry between killing and letting die is nearly always mistakenly applied when people reason about euthanasia. The idea that killing is worse than letting die is derived from the more basic view that actively doing harm is more seriously wrong than merely allowing harm to occur. Killing an innocent person is thus generally more seriously wrong than allowing an innocent person to die because death is generally harmful. Yet in cases in which death would be better for a person than continuing to live, death would not be a harm but would instead be a benefit. And if actively harming is worse than allowing harm to occur, it seems that actively benefiting a person should be better than merely allowing him to benefit. We should therefore expect that in cases in which death would be a benefit to a person rather than a harm and the person wishes to die, killing the person should be, if anything, better than allowing him to die.

In practice this is often true, though for contingent reasons – particularly when a person is, for some reason, such as paralysis, unable to bring about his own death except by allowing himself to die slowly from starvation or dehydration. In such cases it is kinder to kill the person rather than to allow him to die slowly, either in pain or in a wholly or partially sedated state – that is, to practise active rather than passive euthanasia, to employ the usual euphemism for killing for reasons of kindness.

To illustrate my claim about killing, I will cite the last instance in which Jack Kevorkian, the American physician, assisted someone to die. In many previous cases, Kevorkian had assisted people to kill themselves by connecting them to a supply of a lethal chemical which they could then release into their bloodstream. Although he had been brought to trial for this, and the Michigan legislature had even introduced legislation designed specifically to enable a court to convict him if he did it again, juries were never willing to convict him. In 1998, however, he took a further step. The person who sought his assistance in dying was a man in the late stages of amyotrophic lateral sclerosis, which involves progressive weakening and paralysis, who was unable to release the lethal chemical into his own bloodstream and therefore asked Kevorkian do it for him, which Kevorkian then did. All of this was recorded on video. Because in all the previous instances in which he had assisted people in dying, they rather than he had pushed the button to release the chemical, he had never before actually killed someone. But because in this final case he pushed the button himself, Kevorkian killed the man rather than assisting him to kill himself. He was convicted of second-degree homicide and sentenced to 10-25 years in prison. He was paroled after serving more than eight years when he was diagnosed as terminally ill.

What is striking here is that the only difference between the earlier cases and the final one is that in the final case Kevorkian pushed a button at a person's request instead of the person pushing the button himself. That was the difference between killing a person and assisting the person to kill himself. That is, however, clearly a morally trivial difference.

Reflecting on such cases, some people become convinced that the distinctions between letting a person die, enabling a person to kill himself, and killing the person have little or no moral significance when the person requests assistance in dying and death would be good for him and not seriously harmful to others. Yet many of these same people insist on a further condition for the permissibility of any form of assistance in dying. They contend that the person to be assisted must be terminally ill, as was true of the last of the people whom Kevorkian helped to die. But again I think this common view is mistaken. Indeed, it is precisely when a person is not terminally ill that assistance in dying may be most imperative. Those who are terminally ill have the prospect of an early release from their suffering through their illness if they fail to find relief through other means. But those who are not terminally ill but whose lives are intolerable face the prospect of indefinitely protracted suffering. I remember reading years ago of a young woman who was healthy apart from being wholly paralysed and suffering from frequent and excruciatingly painful muscle spasms that could not be relieved except through persistent sedation. She desperately wished to die but was forced by her paralysis to depend on others to bring about her death, which they could do only by killing her or allowing her to starve, to both of which there were legal obstacles. I recall thinking how much crueller it was to deny her euthanasia than to deny it to someone who would die soon in any case.

Dementia

I will conclude by mentioning one final but particularly difficult problem: dementia. Many of us dread the prospect of living on in a state of profound dementia, even if we would be contented (indeed, some of us think that being able to be contented in such a state is part of what would be bad about it). Yet avoiding that state poses special problems, even for those who have both the physical ability and the psychological strength to kill themselves. One such problem is that dementia can occur suddenly, as a result of brain damage. Yet even when it arises gradually, a person who wishes to kill herself before her condition becomes degraded faces the risk of inadvertently passing the point at which she will cease to be able to appreciate her condition and bring her life to an end. Those who are in the early stages of progressive dementia may therefore sometimes feel compelled to end their lives well before they cease to be worth living in order to be certain of avoiding the decline into a degrading state of profound dementia. At least one of the people Kevorkian helped to die came to him while she was still highly competent cognitively precisely because she wanted to be sure to die before her dementia passed beyond this point.

Some people in the early stages of progressive dementia attempt to address this problem by signing an Advance Decision that stipulates that they wish treatment to be withheld from them if they later develop a potentially fatal illness, such as pneumonia, and are incompetent to decide at the time whether to receive treatment. This can give rise to a particularly distressing dilemma if the person does indeed develop such an illness but was contented prior to becoming ill, so that it seems that it would be against her interests to be allowed to die. There are more dimensions to this problem than I can discuss

118

here, such as whether this individual, when demented, has lost so much of what constitute her earlier self as almost to have become a different individual over whose life the wishes of her earlier self have no authority. I will say only that I think the balance of reasons favours honouring the person's earlier autonomous judgment by withholding treatment. That judgment reflects a rational interest the person had and still has in not having the narrative arc of her life as a whole spoiled by a degrading ending.

This essay draws in various places on ideas that are developed and defended at greater length in my book, *The Ethics of Killing: Problems at the Margins of Life,* OUP, 2002.

Dementia and assisted dying

Quentin Fowler

Of all the conditions and illnesses that I might contract as I grow older, I think that the one I fear most is finding that I have been diagnosed with some form of dementia. And as ways are found to conquer cancer and other killers, this is becoming increasingly likely. It is reckoned that, if they live to be in their nineties – and in increasing numbers people do just that – one person in four will suffer from dementia.

Now, let us suppose I have just been told that I am experiencing the early stages of dementia. I ask myself how I might react. I guess I would half know already, but the shock of being told that my suspicions were correct should not be underestimated. The one thing that I hope I would not do is to put my head in the sand and pretend that the medics have got it wrong. It would be marvellous to think I could, in the good old Quaker phrase, 'live adventurously' and see what was coming as a challenge, but whether I would be up to that I am far from certain.

What I would be more likely to do is to ask questions. I would want to have as much information as I could muster about what the future might bring. I know I could not have a complete set of answers to questions such as 'How long have I got to live?' and would have to be content with knowing a number of probabilities –that a quarter would have less than four years to live and three-quarters would survive for up to ten years. I realise that what I would learn would not make for happy reading, such as the fact that I would be facing the so-called 'infantile triad': incontinence of bowel and bladder; inability to communicate; and being spoon-fed.

121

I know that I would have to make a number of adjustments to my life, but I hope I would be able to carry on doing what I had been doing for as long as I was able. I would hope to be continuing to enjoy the challenge of cryptic crosswords, as well as going to a book group of which I was a member. I hope I would recognise that the physical exercise I had been taking was just as important – indeed more so – as the mental exercise. So I would carry on with the Pilates and try to walk at least a mile each day.

However, I would expect to be dipping my toes into activities that were for those who had mental conditions. I know that where I live there are fortnightly sessions lasting two hours called 'Singing for the Brain'. I would expect to be in touch with the local Alzheimer's Society branch, and maybe go to a café they had initiated.

I would also hope that I would be able to talk about my condition. When asked 'How are you?' I would hope I would not give my customary 'Fine, thank you' reply, rather that I would be honest about where I was at. As a Quaker I would hope that I would feel happy that the elders and overseers at my Meeting were aware of what I had been told, and were able to talk to me and amongst themselves about what I might need from them.

Of course I would need support of a more practical nature. I would hope to be able to live in my own home as long as possible. If I were fortunate enough to have a partner, or a family member or a friend who was willing to live with me and support me practically, I would have some breathing space. He or she would have to perform some very basic and often unpleasant tasks, just as one would with a young baby. The chances are that I would require help with feeding myself, and that I would become doubly incontinent. I would need to recognise that he or she would also need support, and a break from me from time to time. I too would be looking for someone else with whom I could meet and talk regularly and with whom I could 'let it all out' from time to time. If I had enough money I could buy in some additional help for my partner or other principal carer in order that I could stay at home as long as possible.

There would be the inevitable but necessary paperwork, which I trust would apply to us all. I would hope that I had made a Will. Just as important to my mind, especially given my diagnosis, is that I had made an Advance Decision. I would need to complete the process whilst I had 'capacity', whilst I had the mental capability of understanding what I was doing. The Advance Decision would cover situations where I could potentially be treated for life-threatening conditions. If I were in an advanced stage of dementia, I would hope that my wishes in the Advance Decision were respected, and that I did not receive the treatment that was being offered. There would also be a need to complete two 'Lasting Power of Attorney' documents, one relating to financial matters, the other to health and welfare. The document covering the health and welfare aspects would allow me to appoint up to three attorneys who would make decisions about my welfare if I were not in a position to make the necessary choices. Included in the document would be a clause directing my attorneys to pay due attention to my wishes, as contained in the Advance Decision, if I were to be in a life-threatening condition.

But, inevitably, dementia would make its unremitting advance. At first, the signs would be only an exaggeration of what had been around previously. Keys would be mislaid; words would be hard to find; objects would turn up in unexpected places; disorientation would occur from time to time. But the time would come when more help was needed than could be arranged at my home, and this would be the time when the move to a 'care home' would be needed.

One would hope that the various options in the vicinity had been explored well in advance, ideally whilst I had a fair degree of capacity. I am sure that I would find that the care being offered – as well as the cost – would vary enormously. It has been said that often such places do not resemble a home and that they offer only a limited amount of care.

If I had a partner or other carer, he or she would as likely as not visit me daily, and help with my feeding, but I know they would be sorely tested, especially when I no longer recognised them. No-one would know how long this situation would last – two, five, ten years? Would my partner have the strength to continue with their daily visits; would they be undertaking them with a sense of duty, and possible resentment? Would they be thinking about the money that was being spent in order to keep someone they had loved dearly simply existing, no longer alive in any meaningful sense of the word? How many young lives in far-away places could be improved by using that money?

Options

What might I be experiencing in the later stages of dementia? There would be double incontinence as already mentioned. I might be unable to recognise those close to me, or even my own reflection. I would be likely to find it difficult to communicate with others, and would gradually lose the power of speech. I would lose the ability to walk, and have an increased risk of a fall. Sooner or later I would have to die and my death might not be pleasant to experience. The most likely cause of my death would not be dementia – it is probable that it would be due to pneumonia, an infection in the lung.

If I were capable of such thoughts I could well be asking myself 'Is this what I want? I have had a full life; would continuing with it be somewhat futile? Yes, I want to stop now, thank you very much.'

But, needless to say, putting such a thought into action is far from easy. There are laws which severely restrict what can be done when someone wishes to end their life – and most people would say rightly so. So, what options would be open to me if I did not want to go into a care home?

I have looked at the various ways I might try if I wished to commit suicide, and have been left with the impression that it is a very dodgy business indeed! Getting it wrong could leave me in an even worse state than I was already in. From what I can gather, the way most likely for me to be successful is for me to go to my doctor and say that I am having trouble sleeping. A mild type of sleeping pill is prescribed. I then return, saying that it is not working and that I need something stronger. I do not use the pills, but start to stockpile them, for use when required. I find this method entirely distasteful. As Quakers, it would run completely counter to our ideas about honesty, and could also involve my doctor being asked questions for which she would be unprepared, due to my dishonesty. So, no, I do not think I would advocate this approach for anyone to adopt.

Of course if I were a doctor I would be likely to know what was needed and be able to put a supply of the requisite pills in a safe place. But as I am not...

Well, I am a quarter Swiss (my maternal grandfather was a Swiss clock-maker) and it could be to Switzerland that I would be looking. My original interest in assisted dying was sparked off by the TV docudrama starring Julie Walters entitled *A Short Stay in Switzerland*. You would be right to ask whether someone with dementia could be considered as a potential candidate for Dignitas. From what I have read, a number of people in that situation have been accepted. Going to Zurich would be quite a challenge for me and for whoever was accompanying me. Getting the timing right would not be easy – too late and I might no longer have the mental capacity required; too early and I would be losing precious months when I could enjoy living a reasonably normal life. I would have to get the application off in good time, in order that Dignitas could process it, and again timing would be of the essence. Going to Dignitas is not cheap; I would need to be able to find the £10,000 or so required for the venture. Whether I would have the mental and emotional capital required is another question; I think I would have but who knows when the chips are down? I would have to find the strength to say goodbye to those who had come on this journey with me, and I would need to find the resolve to drink the final draught.

Of course this is a momentous step for anyone to take and I would need to talk it through on a number of occasions with family and friends, and in particular with anyone who was accompanying me to Switzerland. Assisting someone to commit suicide is against the law, and anyone who became involved in what I was asking them to do could face questioning by the police. In theory they could be prosecuted – though the chances of this are slim if it was established early on that they were motivated only by compassion.

So far I have only looked at what options I have under the law as it stands now in England and Wales. But what options should I have? Can we look at a Brave New World in which fundamental principles are translated into law?

Autonomy and compassion

Can I first of all ask whether there should be a distinctly Christian, or more specifically a uniquely Quaker view on the question of assisted dying? My belief is that this is a humanitarian issue, and that ideally all people, whether they possess a faith or not, should be able to come together in examining this question.

What are those fundamental principles which determine how we should address this issue? I believe they are firstly autonomy and secondly compassion.

By autonomy in this context I am meaning that everyone should be able to decide for him- or herself, as far as they are able, when, how and where they are going to die. Of course, there will be many people for whom, because of the nature of their illness or other circumstance, such a choice will not be possible. But where it is, and when the person concerned still has capacity and has been able to demonstrate that this intention is a fixed one, that choice should be theirs and theirs alone. There would be a range of people in such a situation. There would be those with a terminal illness with less than six months to live, as proposed in recent Bills brought without success before Parliament. There would be those with a long-term progressive illness, such as Parkinson's disease. And there would also be those in the early stages of dementia. I believe that, for all such people, where they have shown that they have a clear and fixed desire to die, they should have access to the means to end their lives at a time of their choosing.

By compassion in this context, I am looking at the involvement of other people in the actual process of bringing about a person's death. The philosopher John Stuart Mill put forward the proposition that the state should only intervene when one of its citizens threatened to harm others. So if an act is solely motivated by compassion, it would seem that, if you accept Mill's proposition, any person assisting the suicide of another should not be prosecuted. There can be two types of assistance in the context of assisted dying. First, there is the help provided by a doctor in prescribing the appropriate medicine to bring about the death of the person concerned. Second, there is the help provided by another person when the individual who is wishing to die cannot physically do what is required to bring about the outcome they desire. Both types of assistance are motivated by compassion and it follows that both should attract the protection of the law from prosecution.

I realise that many Christians, and also many Quakers, whether they think of themselves as Christian or not, will struggle with the position that I am proposing. 'Thou shalt not kill' is inscribed firmly onto our moral compass. But Christ's injunction to 'Love others as one loves oneself' should surely be written even more strongly onto our heart. So, how in this Brave New World I have envisaged, would I see myself ending my life if I were to be diagnosed with dementia?

I am suggesting that I would initiate the process at an early stage, while I still had the mental wherewithal to understand what was happening. I would expect to be questioned on more than one occasion in order to confirm that I was absolutely determined on the course I wished to take. I would then be supplied with the requisite medicine, and the instructions for taking it. Then, when I considered I had begun to lose what dignity I still possessed and that life no longer had very much to offer, I would hope to arrange a time when my family could be around me in my home and I could say my final goodbyes before downing the welcome draught. That surely must be a good death.

Further perspectives on dementia

Judy Kessler

1. Our Quaker meeting, like many others, has a group of single elderly women who watch out for each other and share information. The group has a warm sense of community.

The needs of members of a group such as this change as they get older and a move into sheltered accommodation or into a care home can be a relief or a necessity – or both.

The approach of dementia is a concern for us all. Living alone may mean that a family is widespread and far-flung. How can these blood relatives know what is going on? This question is especially important when we know a visit from a loved one will rejuvenate an elderly person. The friendship network will be more up-to-date and informed. Close friends can often recognise the symptoms of dementia which start and grow. As the dementia develops, those people who are not relatives have very limited ways in which they can help with the necessary life changes. More and more of us are living alone and we need to develop networks of care and responsibility.

2. I live alone. I fear the onset of dementia, because I witnessed it in both my parents and have seen the devastation it caused to the family. I have written an Advance Decision. There is not much more I can do except recognise that if dementia occurs I want to recognise it for what it is and take action myself to terminate my life. I have made a list of ten things which would make my life unbearable. I have reached some of these milestones already. However, I want my actions to be legitimate. I have discussed my views with my family and they seem to prefer my proposed course of action as opposed to the repetition of the process of caring for my parents. I certainly do.

Life and death

Anne Wade

When I was nine my father put my dog down. She had heart failure and was breathless and slow, but she was not in pain. She loved my little sister and me sitting stroking her, and she was contented. But she was inconvenient – she dribbled as she went out to pee. I suggested she could live on the veranda, which would be easy to clean. My mother said, 'She does not really want to live like this – if she could talk, she would ask us to help her die.' I thought, 'How do you know? If I could talk, I would want to be allowed to die in my own time, to be kept clean and comfortable, to be loved and held. Would you put me down when I am old if I am slow and wet my knickers?'

I decided then that I would learn how to care for people who were dying, and live my life simply so I would always have time for people, so no one I loved would feel they had to kill themselves rather than be a nuisance. This is what assisted dying means to me: assisting people to live well for as long as they can, and then to die comfortably and as well as they are able.

I have been privileged to be with many dying people. Now I can no longer do very much and it will soon be my turn. Yes, there are some frightening stories, but we need to face our fears and find out how much truth there is in them. One of the things I have learned is that dying peacefully and well is the norm, even in a hospital. And there are various things we can all set in place, individually and as a society, to make it more likely to happen as we wish. What I have also learned is that it is not safe to give anyone the power to kill other people.

Concerns

So, why should we legalise assisted suicide, or active euthanasia, for those who are no longer able to kill themselves? The main arguments are about autonomy and 'unbearable suffering'. Many people are afraid they may die helpless, in pain, with no dignity or quality of life and no longer with the capacity to commit suicide; or that a loved one will be in this position and they will have to watch helplessly or may be asked to kill them; so they want suicide to be made easier and the threat of prosecution removed.

Whatever we think about changing the law, these are valid concerns. We would all hate to be in these situations. I want us to consider other solutions than suicide.

People speak of wanting to die with dignity 'when suffering becomes unbearable at the end of life' as if that were the norm, and yet this rarely happens. Good medical and nursing care can keep most people comfortable without drugging them to stupor. Gerald Priestland, the Quaker and BBC correspondent, talked about crying when he was incontinent after a stroke and how liberating it was to learn how to accept help. Above all, people need love, as well as competent care. Intractable pain, at any age, often stems from feeling lonely and unloved. Where family and friends are insufficient, a hospice is skilled in alleviating this misery.

The hard part is earlier, when we realise our options are closing … that is when we grieve. And then we deal with it and learn to live well within our limitations. Life is continuous loss and discovery, and death is just one more step. Maybe we miss something important if we try to shortcut it.

If we were to go down the road of assisted suicide and active euthanasia, we would inevitably create a society that would make a good natural death more difficult for anyone to achieve, just as routine medicalisation of childbirth made natural birth seem idiosyncratic.

What is a good death like?

I became a Quaker when I was seventeen, and the following year I helped someone in my Meeting to care for her dying mother. I did not expect to be much use, as I was inexperienced, impractical and not good at being chatty. But she was very easy to love, she liked having me there, and it was a great gift for me. I only had to be with her, to do any little thing she asked for so that she was comfortable, to hold and move her very gently, and to learn to tolerate sitting doing nothing – without reading (that was the hard part) – so that I was fully 'there'. I tried to let her feel our love, reassuring her, when she was apologetic, that no one felt she was a nuisance, and that we were glad to spend time with her – which was true. I tried to centre down and be with her in the way I tried to be in Quaker Meetings for Worship.

No one interfered with her process, except to keep her clean and comfortable. She was helped to eat and drink but it was not forced on her. She was frail but not in much pain, and she was not drugged, which helped her stay alert and focused, though in a deep place. She was in a sunny room overlooking the garden. She wanted no occupation or entertainment. She did not want fuss or noise or music or distraction, and my lack of small talk was an asset. She seemed to me to be doing something important. She was dying a natural death, and I was learning from her how to die.

I became a nurse, and sat with many dying people. I felt privileged to be with them in such an important part of their lives. Most, though not drugged, seemed unaware that they were dying, and just drifted out of life. I would sit with them in the same way, keeping them clean and comfortable, keeping their mouths moist, holding their hand, centring down and being fully there with them.

Some knew they were dying, and most were not afraid at that point. If they were, I could calm them. Sometimes relatives were there, and I would encourage them to sit and hold them. I realised that what I could do mattered, even within an imperfect system. A relatively ignorant and powerless young woman, I could still give someone the human touch and warmth that made dying easier, and take them down into the depths where everything is all right.

Life is extraordinary

Are these faith-based arguments? Being a Quaker influences my ways of caring and helps me keep my life coherent and simple, but Quakers have a range of views on this as on most topics. My arguments are not religious, but experiential – from lived experience. Integrity, valuing people equally, competent kindness, meaning in our lives, communities that work for everyone – these are the things we all want, the values of every decent human being, and we all struggle to find the best way of expressing them.

Life is something extraordinary from anyone's point of view, to be cherished, not to be terminated on grounds of expediency. It does not require a religious outlook to believe that no one – young, old, disabled, feckless – should be dismissed as an uneconomic member of society and therefore useless and possibly to be put down.

One of the most radiant, lovable people I have known was completely demented and deteriorated, but in an unkind institution everyone loved her and was kind to her, and was a bit happier for making her comfortable. How can we live so we end up like that, even if our minds go?

Published with the permission of 'the Friend' where the article appeared in the issue of 4 September 2015.

The ministry of dying – reflections on death row

Jan Arriens

Some years ago I was asked to write to a prisoner on death row in the USA whom I didn't know, in an effort to talk him out of dropping his appeals. He had been on death row for a long time – about twelve years – and felt his situation had become intolerable. His appeals were simply stringing the process out, and he had no close relatives.

To begin with, my letter rehearsed all the familiar arguments: never give up hope, don't give in to the system, cling on to life, think of the effect on those dear to you. But the more I got into the letter, the more that these arguments seemed hollow. Trying to put myself into his position, it felt as though I was trying to deprive him of the one power that was still left him: deciding on his own fate. He was bound to die anyway, but by dropping his appeals he was in control and forcing the state to act in accordance with his wishes.

This was, I suppose, a form of assisted dying. Or, more strictly, euthanasia, as the means of death was to be administered not by the prisoner himself but by others. It was certainly not physician-assisted dying, for it is prison officials who pull the levers or press the buttons to start the lethal injection process, while the role of the physician is confined to that of certifying death. Thus state-sanctioned killing is sanitised.

That may seem a little extreme, but we are all under sentence of death. When, as with the prisoner, it becomes clear that our end is imminent, one of the few elements of control we retain is to choose the time and manner of our going. At the same time, I have every sympathy for those in the medical and nursing professions who are closely involved with the process of death, e.g. those working in hospices. They will be acutely aware of the extraordinary things that can happen in the final stages of life and the need to approach death sacramentally and with reverence.

I am thinking in particular of an acquaintance of mine, a resolute atheist, who died of cancer. A Friend and I went to visit him in a nursing home. He was surrounded comfortably by some of his own pictures and ornaments. He was quite clear that the end was not far off and, as an avowed sceptic of anything spiritual beyond our normal world, might have been the kind of person who would calmly have hastened his end.

Instead, our friend underwent a number of profound experiences in those last days that completely changed his attitude towards the meaning of life and hence towards death. He was totally lucid and did not believe that the medication he was on had affected his mind. In one 'vision', he had been surprised to meet Jesus. This was not a gentle figure in a flowing robe but a short, swarthy and feisty figure, very Jewish, who was upset by the way his teachings had been traduced. In another, two circles had gradually merged in a way that held profound significance for him. The upshot of this and other experiences he had had was that he had totally lost any fear of death and viewed things quite differently from before. Joyfully he told us how life had become full of meaning for him. He was certain about this, although not in a way that he could put into words.

Afterwards the two of us went for a walk to reflect on the extraordinary change that had come over our friend. As we walked in the hills, we both felt enveloped in a kind of dancing, light and benevolent atmosphere – at once palpable and unlike anything either of us had felt before. Our friend died three days later.

While death is not always attended by such deep revelations, there is a strong case to be made for allowing life to run its natural course. As Sarah Dodgson has written (*the Friend*, 12 June 2015), a 'person in a coma still has a soul in his body until he dies. And that soul needs care and ministry, even if the neurologists assure us that there is no awareness going on in there, as they understand it. So, for me it makes perfect sense to sing a religious lullaby to a soul to make it go to sleep.'

I am reminded here of some of the most powerful ministry I have ever heard in Meeting. A retired doctor stood up to say that his son in South Africa was in a coma and expected to die. His sister had been summoned to the bedside. Not really knowing what to do, she had sung the Lord's Prayer to her brother, who was meant to be totally beyond reach, and was also an unbeliever. Tears rolled down the son's cheeks. Struggling to contain his emotion, the doctor said that medically he knew this kind of response was impossible – and yet clearly there had been communication of some kind.

No doubt it would have been possible for the life-support machine to have been switched off and for the son to have died before all this happened. Then again, I cannot but help feel that there are circumstances in which the prolongation of life involves marked suffering and brings no discernible benefit, and where we should leave the choice to the person who is dying. Sarah Dodgson sums it all up perfectly when she says, 'For me, the ministry to the soul does not always mean keeping it alive in the world. I would not impose that worldview on someone else, but it is offered as a saving grace to counter the "life at all costs" thinking currently imposed by law.'

Such a change would, however, need to be done with great sensitivity. A great many safeguards would need to be firmly in place if we are to avoid confusion, mistakes, distress, alarm and a breakdown of trust between those nearing death and their carers.

It is a decision that is not confined to the individual concerned; it also has a bearing on those around him or her. It asks others to bear emotional burdens or assume additional responsibilities. All that, ultimately, is a matter for the law, but if assisted dying does become possible in some form or another, then we as Quakers can add the additional element of our group processes and discernment. This might take the form of support from elders and overseers and a meeting for clearness. Only if that process brought a clear sense of unity and that we were not violating spiritual principles and the process of preparation for death should we then proceed.

Those principles would draw heavily on our testimonies, especially those to peace, truth and simplicity. Peace not in the sense of the avoidance of war, but of an inner equanimity and knowledge that one was proceeding from the right place. Truth in the sense that we were facing the inevitable – death – with realism and acceptance, and were not elevating life into something to be extended at all costs. And simplicity, in allowing ourselves to depart from this life graciously and without fuss, as something in the natural order of things. If life becomes insupportable – either physically or psychologically – we avail ourselves of the means available, but subject always to a process of profound discernment and a sharing deeply grounded in our testimonies. And they in turn are grounded in that sense of connection with what the Quaker writer Rufus Jones called the 'Great Beyond'.

Strange things happen when we approach death. The mind, it seems, is often in harmony with the body. We do not generally rage against the dying night but move towards the end with acceptance.

Here, once again, the death row experience can be instructive. A prisoner with whom I correspond, and who has been on death row for over thirty years, has seen many men go to their deaths. Mike writes:

> I really do worry about how hard it will be on those close to me when they sign my death warrant. Myself, I guess I take more of a Buddhist approach to the whole concept of death – it's just not something I'm concerned about and if that's what is to come, then so be it.
>
> I'm sure a lot of my attitude towards that probable event is influenced by my own experience the last time I was on death watch (this was in 1988 when he came within hours of being executed and had a profound mystical experience – JA). I've also been thinking that my attitude is not really that uncommon among the death row population as a whole, although obviously my own experience was unique and not shared by others.
>
> But yet what I realise is that there is a certain measure of indifference, even complacency, towards the thought of

death amongst all of us. I cannot recall anyone who knew that their death warrant might soon issue, or those who actually did have their warrant signed, showing any real emotional signs. In fact, many even welcomed it. And although I've read a lot over the years about the process and those speaking of long-term solitary confinement, I cannot recall reading anything about why it is that those sentenced to death really are not that upset when their time comes and this has me somewhat curious.

I suppose it's really not that different from the resolve most cancer patients feel when they too are counting down their last days – especially those who have suffered for so long under that threat of death, and when that final countdown does come, there's almost a sense of relief that the journey may finally come to an end and the suffering will finally pass.

But then there's those who we must leave behind, and they are the ones that really suffer – just as with anyone who experiences the death of someone you care about.

I do not think that these remarkable words signify resignation or weariness, although both those elements are present. It is something deeper, like the way in which the mind moves in concert with the body as our physical powers fail. People on death row spend years with the threat of death hanging over them. They are forced, in an almost monastic way, to contemplate their end. Death is ever present. The result is a subtle change, in which death is no longer seen as something quite so momentous but becomes incorporated into our conscious existence as a natural extension. This is not far removed from the approach towards dying within the Buddhist tradition based around the Tibetan Book of the Dead.

Where death can be assimilated into life as a natural process with potentially deep spiritual meaning, we should, I feel, do all we can to allow the end to come along those lines. But there are also instances – and, based on the Dutch experience, I think these are rare – where people can go to their deaths seeking help when the prospect of further suffering has become too much and they are denied the means of ending their lives unaided. That too we should respect, and they too can do so in a state of spiritual grace.

Appendix (i)

1. The law in the UK

The Suicide Act 1961 decriminalised the act of suicide in England and Wales so that those who failed in the attempt to kill themselves would no longer be prosecuted. It also stated that 'a person who aids, abets, counsels or procures the suicide of another, or attempt by another to commit suicide shall be liable on conviction on indictment to imprisonment for a term not exceeding fourteen years.' The Suicide Act 1961 applies only to England and Wales. Under Scots Law a person who assists a suicide might be charged with murder, culpable homicide, or no offence depending upon the facts of each case.

2. Recent attempts to change and clarify the law in the UK

a)   Assisted Dying Bill (Lord Falconer), presented June 2014
Lord Falconer's Assisted Dying Bill mirrored the law as enacted in Oregon (see below). It was tabled in the House of Lords in June 2014, and received its Second Reading on 18 July 2014. During a debate lasting over nine hours the Bill was examined in detail but not voted on. The Bill had its first day of Committee Stage on 7 November 2014, during which the House of Lords accepted the principle of law change and voted in unanimous support for an amendment to the Bill, put down by Lord Pannick, which set out a model for judicial oversight of assisted dying. This required a judge in the family division of the High Court to confirm that a terminally ill patient, with less than six months to live, had reached 'a voluntary, clear, settled and informed' decision to control the time and manner of their death.

(b) Assisted Dying Bill (Rob Marris), presented September 2015

On 11 September 2015 a Private Member's Bill was introduced in the House of Commons by Rob Marris MP. After a four hour debate, it was defeated, on a free vote, by a substantial majority.

(c) Debbie Purdy – request for clarification of the law, 2009

Debbie Purdy (1963–2014) was a British music journalist and political activist from Bradford with primary progressive multiple sclerosis, notable for her challenge to the law in England and Wales as it relates to assisted suicide. Debbie Purdy and her counsel, David Pannick QC, argued that the Director of Public Prosecutions was infringing her human rights by failing to clarify how the Suicide Act is enforced. Purdy's particular concern was to discover if any actions her husband, Omar Puente, took in assisting her suicide would lead to his prosecution. The Law Lords accepted in 2009 that Debbie Purdy had a right to know whether her husband would be prosecuted if he helped her to travel abroad to commit suicide.

(d) Director of Public Prosecutions clarification, 2010

As a consequence of the Law Lords' judgement the previous year (see above), in February 2010, the Director of Public Prosecutions issued the prosecuting policy on cases of 'Encouraging or Assisting Suicide'.The policy includes a detailed list of public interest factors that will influence the decision on whether or not to prosecute someone for assisting a suicide.

A prosecution is less likely if the assisted person made a voluntary, well informed decision to end their life, and if the assister was wholly motivated by compassion. Furthermore, if they had sought to dissuade the person from suicide, and if their actions may be

145

characterised as reluctant encouragement or assistance, prosecution is less likely.

Prosecution is more likely if the person committing suicide was under 18 years of age; if they lacked the mental capacity to reach an informed decision to end their life; or if they were physically able to undertake the act without assistance.

The policy instructs police and prosecutors to adopt a 'common sense' approach to the issue of financial gain. If it is shown that compassion was the only driving force behind the assister's actions, the fact that they may have 'gained' some benefit will not usually be treated as a factor in favour of prosecution.

3. Law and practice in Oregon and other USA states

<u>Law passed in Oregon, 1996</u>

For a person to qualify for consideration under Oregon's Death with Dignity Act:
- the patient must be 18 years or older, mentally competent and diagnosed with a terminal illness that will lead to their death within six months;
- the patient must request life-ending medication twice, with fifteen days separating each request (a 'cooling off' period); must make a written request to their doctor which is witnessed by two individuals who are not primary care-givers or family members; and
- the patient must be able to self-administer and ingest the life-ending medication him- or herself.

- The diagnosis of a terminal illness for a patient with less than six months to live must be certified by a consulting doctor, who must also certify that the patient is mentally competent to make and communicate health care decisions;
- if either doctor determines that the patient's judgement is impaired the patient would either be deemed ineligible for assistance or they could be referred for psychological evaluation; and
- the attending doctor must inform the patient of alternatives, including palliative care, hospice and pain management options.

Assisted dying in practice, 1996 – 2014, in Oregon

In the eighteen years that assisted dying has been legal in Oregon there have been no calls to extend the law beyond terminally ill, mentally competent adults.

A report on the workings of Oregon's Death with Dignity Act (2015) showed that in 2014:

- 105 people died from ingesting medications prescribed in 2014 or in the two previous years. This accounts for around 0.3% of total deaths in Oregon;
- 155 people requested life-ending medication during 2014: 50 did not take the medication – many of them took comfort in knowing the option was there, and
- the majority of people (69%) who had an assisted death had terminal cancer and most (68%) were aged 65 or over.
- Laws supporting assisted dying have been passed in three other USA states: Washington, Vermont and California.

4. Law and practice in Switzerland

Dignitas is a Swiss group, helping those with medically diagnosed severe or terminal illnesses, and unendurable disabilities, to die, assisted by qualified doctors and nurses. Dignitas has helped over 1700 people of various nationalities to die in clinics in Zurich (60% of whom were German and 15% were British). Dignitas can arrange the option of an accompanied suicide for anyone who joins their organisation, provided he or she meets a number of criteria. These include: the patient must be mentally competent; be able to carry out the final action which brings about death him or herself; and have sent a written request to Dignitas (see http://www.dignitas.ch). It should be noted that there are other groups in Switzerland offering services of this kind.

5. Law in Belgium and other European countries

According to the Belgian law on euthanasia passed on 28 May 2002, the major legal requirements for performing euthanasia are:

- repeated and consistent requests from an adult patient who is competent (that is, who has full mental capacity), made under no external pressure and in writing (or expressed in a written Advance Directive in the case of a patient in an irreversible state of unconsciousness);
- persistent and intolerable physical and/or mental suffering, caused by an irreversible medical condition (due to an accident or to a disease).

The law in Holland (2002) and Luxembourg (2009) is similar to that in Belgium.

6. Comparison of criteria adopted in Oregon, Switzerland and Belgium

	Oregon	Switzerland	Belgium
Foreigners eligible?	No	Yes	No
Minimum age	18	No age limit for minors	18 (12 in Holland)
Self-administer?	Yes	Yes	No - carried out by a doctor
Terminal illness?	Applicants **must** have less than 6 months to live	Yes - possibility	Yes - possibility
In severe pain?	Usually, but not necessarily so	Yes - possibility	'Persistent and intolerable suffering'
Severe disability?	Not a criterion	Yes - possibility	Yes - possibility
Applicants can be elderly and have many ailments?	Not a criterion	Yes - possibility	Yes - possibility
Can applicants have a psychiatric condition?	Not a criterion	Yes, including: Alzheimer's/ Dementia; Psychoses; Severe Depression; Bipolar disorder	Yes – 'Persistent and intolerable suffering, physical and/or mental'
Must patient have capacity?	Yes	Yes	Yes – or if not, to have signed an Advance Directive

7. Campaigning and information-providing organisations

Dignity in Dying
181 Oxford Street, London, W1D 2JT
020-7479-7730
www.dignityindying.org.uk
The main campaigning organisation in England and Wales to legalise assisted dying for terminally ill adults.

Care not Killing
6 Marshalsea Road
London SE1 1HL
020-7234-9680
www.carenotkilling.org.uk
A campaigning group opposed to voluntary euthanasia and doctor-assisted suicide.

Compassion in Dying
181 Oxford Street, London, W1D 2JT
0800-999-2434
www.compassionindying.org.uk
A charity which provides free Advance Decision packs.

Not dead yet
www.notdeadyet.org.uk
Disability activists opposed to the legalisation of assisted suicide

Appendix (ii)

Leeds Research

The research was conducted over 18 months in 2012–14 under the auspices of the University of Leeds and with the consent of Leeds Area Quaker Meeting (LAQM). It came about because of the concern expressed in Area Meeting and the work undertaken by LAQM's end-of-life care working party over the previous two years.

The focus of the research was on Quaker views of end-of-life care and on assisted dying within that context. It followed the Quaker methods of addressing a concern to achieve clarity and looked for a range of views held by Quakers in the Leeds area. Qualitative and quantitative sociological methods were used to supplement the Quaker process and to provide insights into the reasons for the decisions and choices made.

There was evidence of deep-seated anxiety about how one might experience the end of life. Most people wished for some autonomy and choice within a palliative care system, especially if there was extreme pain or dementia at the end.

There was a unanimous wish to see an expansion of holistic palliative care as demonstrated within the best hospices, but a sad realisation that this was unlikely to be evident within our lifetimes. There was a realisation that those who are middle class and articulate are more likely to be able to access this care. This was felt to be against our testimony on equality.

There were strong feelings both for and against assisted dying. However, most people wanted the law to be changed to allow choice, provided that there were clear safeguards. Any change in the law should take place in parallel with an increase in the availability of palliative care.

It was evident that people thought it essential to talk with friends, family and medical practitioners about their wishes, fears and concerns well in advance of need, and to ensure that all practical eventualities had been covered by the writing of a Will, an Advance Decision and Lasting Power of Attorney. Most people welcomed the opportunity that the research gave them to discuss these issues.

The discussions in the six focus groups that were held in local meetings indicated that Quakers in Leeds feel that debate about assisted dying is now as much within the social context as in the legal and political spheres. It is a topic which increasing numbers of people wish to talk about, and there is a growing realisation of its connections with health care, demographic trends and the issue of choice.

The research findings contributed to the work of LAQM's end-of-life care working party and to the literature on assisted dying. To access further information about the research see www.leedsquakers.org.uk. (Go to 'Activities' and click on 'Dying and Death').

Judy Kessler

Selected bibliography

Brewer, C. and Irwin, M. (eds) (2015) *I'll See Myself Out, Thank You*, Newbold on Stour: Skyscraper Publications. *Consists of thirty personal views in support of assisted suicide. Most of the contributions are lively and challenging.*

Gawande, A. (2015) *Being Mortal: Medicine and What Matters in the End. Provides a critique of modern medicine's failure to improve the process of life's ending. Very readable. The author gave the Reith lectures in 2014 on 'The Idea of Wellbeing'.*

Howarth, G. (ed) (2007) *Death and Dying: A Sociological Introduction*, Cambridge: Polity Press. *Looks at key issues in the sociology of death and dying. A comprehensive and accessible discussion of key topics.*

Jackson, E. and Keown, J. (2012) *Debating Euthanasia*, Oxford: Hart Publishing. *A clear, detailed and accessible reasoning both for and against euthanasia.*

Kübler-Ross, E. (1995) *Death is of vital importance,* New York, NY: Station Hill Press. *A warm and sophisticated book dealing with why death and dying is important both to the individual and the wider family.*

Quaker faith & practice (2013)*: The book of Christian discipline of the Yearly Meeting of the Religious Society of Friends (Quakers) in Britain.* Fifth edition. London: Religious Society of Friends (Quakers) in Britain.

Romain, J. (ed) (2014) *Assisted Dying. Rabbinic Responses*, London: The Movement for Reform Judaism. *Contributions by seventeen reform and liberal rabbis, arguing for and against assisted dying.*

Seale, C. (1998) *Constructing Death: the Sociology of Dying and Bereavement,* Cambridge: Cambridge University Press. *This book analyses the experiences of those dying, and the bereaved and institutional responses to death.*

Youngner, S. and Kimsma, G. (eds) (2012) *Physician-Assisted Death in Perspective: Assessing the Dutch Experience*, Cambridge: Cambridge University Press. *A comprehensive report and analysis of the Dutch euthanasia experience over the last thirty years looking at empirical data and real life clinical behaviour.*